SACRED SPACES

SUBTLE SHIFTS FOR MIND, BODY, AND HOME TRANSFORMATION

COLLEEN AVIS

FEATURING: DR. JILL PIERCE BEASLEY, HERMON BLACK,
PAMELA BOLADO, LAURA DI FRANCO, TANSY JANE DOWMAN,
BRETT EATON, JAMIE EDWARDS, JEN GRISWOLD,
CHRISTINA KAUFFMANN, ANN KEATING, MICOLE NOBLE,
LYNNE FLETCHER O'BRIEN, DR. SAM PAPPAS, ALISON QUALTER,
TANYA SAUNDERS, RORRIE SISK, OLIVIA SMITH,
ANGELA BARBIERI USAS, LISA VRANCKEN, LISA WILSON

Sacred Spaces

Subtle Shifts for Mind, Body, and Home Transformation

Colleen Avis

©Copyright 2022 Colleen Avis

Published by Brave Healer Productions

Print ISBN: 978-1-954047-42-6

eBook ISBN: 978-1-954047-43-3

DEDICATION

To the Sacred Space authors, thank you for bringing this dream to life.
I admire and respect you and am grateful for your trust, dedication,
and transparency in sharing a piece of your amazing self in this book.
Your individual strengths and unique approach to life
make this world a better place.

To Duncan and Finn, you two know me better than I know myself;
how'd I get so lucky to have you both cheering me on?
Thank you for allowing me to be me. I love you more.

To Mom, without your strength and love, I wouldn't be me.
Thanks for being you. I love you.

DISCLAIMER

This book offers health and nutritional information and is designed for educational purposes only. You should not rely on this information as a substitute for, nor does it replace professional medical advice, diagnosis, or treatment. If you have any concerns or questions about your health, you should always consult with a physician or other healthcare professional. Do not disregard, avoid, or delay obtaining medical or health-related advice from your healthcare professional because of something you may have read here. The use of any information provided in this book is solely at your own risk.

Developments in medical research may impact the health, fitness, and nutritional advice that appears here. No assurances can be given that the information contained in this book will always include the most relevant findings or developments with respect to the particular material.

Having said all that, know that the experts here have shared their tools, practices, and knowledge with you with a sincere and generous intent to assist you on your health and wellness journey. Please contact them with any questions you may have about the techniques or information they provided. They will be happy to assist you further!

TABLE OF CONTENTS

INTRODUCTION

You are sacred space. You are perfect as you are and there is nothing to fix. You are not broken. You are on a beautiful journey, and where and what you are matters.

Sacred Spaces is an energetic collection of unique stories and powerful practices shared by a group of courageous authors. Each word and experience reflect their hearts and souls, sharing with you a piece of their journey, hoping it will create space for you to feel inspired.

VULNERABILITY. COLLECTIVE. IMPACT.

Heart and soul created this book and was inspired by a few core intentions.

- Each author bravely leaned into their vulnerabilities and shared an intimate piece of their life story. For many, this personal and private process, "Oh my God, what did I get into?" required breaking open our hearts and trusting, you the reader, to be supportive as we learned more deeply about ourselves.

- Second, trust in the collective group, joining together to support each other, even though we were first, mainly strangers. We were vulnerable with and trusted each other, knowing that together a universal ripple rooted in compassion, kindness, and love would multiply and energetically provide a greater reach and impact.

- Third, we believe the sacred space this book creates is all worth it if one reader feels impacted, loved, related to, or acts to move forward and make a subtle shift toward their own transformation.

These intentions—bravery, vulnerability, trust, love, action, and belief—created the sacred space you hold in your hands. It's the same sacred space that resides in you. You are a sacred space filled with all you need; the universe guarantees it.

Too often in our daily lives, we look to the outside world to provide a sense of validation, acceptance, and self-worth. We worry about what others think or how others may interpret our choices, and we attach value to these outside opinions.

Only you know yourself intimately. Therefore, the stories and tools in this book offer you an opportunity to learn from another person's experience, and only you will determine how it will empower, impact, shape, strengthen, or challenge your own story.

We hope you see and know the power within you that already exists, the power that enables healing and transformation. We hope you recognize that you are your own best healer, able to transform your mind, body, and home.

Before you dive into the stories here, close your eyes and repeat to yourself:

I am sacred space. I am perfect as I am, and there is nothing to fix.

I am not broken. I am on a journey, and where and what I am matters.

CHAPTER 1

THE SACRED SPACE OF SELF

A COMPREHENSIVE WELLNESS TOOLKIT

Colleen Avis, Integrative Life Coach, Mindfulness Mentor, Yoga Guide

MY STORY

THE VIEW

The inside space of the grocery store garbage dumpster was dim, gray, and surprisingly clean, at least from what I could see at dusk that evening. *This is not going to be pleasant; I know this damn dumpster is full of slimy, rancid, mushy trash.* I anticipated a hot steamy concoction of decaying food and an odor that would haunt me for decades, but as my mom hoisted me into the dumpster, that's not what I found. Or maybe it was, but at 16 years old, I was more focused on getting in and out quickly, so no one saw me.

Industrial-sized black trash bags, full of bruised, oddly shaped, and unwrapped produce, day-old baked goods, dented canned goods and damaged boxes of pasta filled the dumpster. Surprisingly, the inside of this dumpster felt somewhat organized; in a way, it was similar to well-placed items on shelves inside the store. Don't get me wrong, the selection was limited, and trash bags replaced shelves, but the bread was all in one bag, cans in another, fruit and vegetables in another. *It's not that bad in here. I gotta get out of here so no one sees me.*

It reminded me of the food pantry where we regularly collected five-pound blocks of Velveeta cheese loaf, industrial-sized peanut butter (*yes crunchy this time!*), bags of generic Toasty O's, and bars of soap. Their donation receiving area was full of unsorted bags, just like the ones in this dumpster.

In the late 80s, on a nightly basis, our local grocery stores threw damaged and expired items in dumpsters behind the store, and in the morning, they were collected and taken to the dump. Unlike today, they were unlocked and pretty easy to access.

THE TEAM

"Hey Col, be careful in there, reach up if you need me." said my mom smiling, attempting to hide the shake in her voice. Getting in and out of a dumpster is tricky. "I got it, Mom, don't worry." *You gotta be strong; they need you to be strong.*

A tight shallow breath reminds me of our uncertainty, my mom holding tightly to my little brothers' hand. *Sheesh, Mom, it's okay; stop squeezing his hand so tight.* My little brother loved the adventure of finding food in the dumpster. "Col, drop another one to me; I'll put it in our shopping bag!"

Our team worked through many dumpster-like challenges together.

When my biological father abandoned our family, I grew up quickly. It was abrupt, out of the blue, full-on cease-to-support-us, you-don't-matter-to-me, gone. There were no warning signs, no years of watching my parents arguing or yelling at each other, and no nights he didn't come home. My parents didn't have periods of separation. Honestly, that would have made things easier to understand. He was just gone, leaving no financial or emotional support.

For 17 years, my mom stayed at home, taking care of the house, making sure we had what we needed for school: taking me to soccer, piano, and dance lessons, healthy meals, especially breakfast. *Hot baked apples with cinnamon … my favorite; oh I can still smell them.*

When he left, she showed new skills—resourceful, resilient, and determined bad-ass skills—that for some time included a combination of food pantry visits and dumpster diving so we could eat. There was safe and edible food in the bottom of a dumpster.

I smile even now, recalling how it was somewhat of a game trying to find food in the dumpster that no longer had labels identifying the contents. Looking up from the bottom and over the edge was my mom, laughing, "What did you find?" My brother giggled, jumping up and down like we had arrived at Disneyland. We were hopeful yet entertained the possibility that when we got home and opened the damaged and unlabeled cans, they may all be green beans. *That must have happened a dozen times!*

We laughed, loved, and learned a lot; it wasn't always easy after he left, but we found our way.

THE WORDS

"You're not worth the f*cking skin you live in." His final words to me still echo in my mind turning my gut in knots, creating numbing disbelief across every inch of my body. I will never forget or understand why he chose to abandon us. *Does anyone understand why a parent would leave their child behind?*

Self-sabotaging was a tool I mastered to mask the scars his leaving offered me. He showed me abandonment, then I learned and perfected it. I abandoned my moral compass, thoughts, body, and emotions. I moved too quickly in relationships and then abandoned them when they no longer served me, or I could no longer control them.

THE EXPERIENCES

In my early 20s, I struggled with eating disorders, pushing away what I didn't want to experience and emotions I didn't want to show the world. This behavior accompanied my desperation to be included and loved by others, so I perfected people-pleasing. I abandoned my boundaries and believed I could fix others' struggles, pouring myself into helping them, which pushed people away and added to my fears. I desperately wanted to climb out of the figurative dumpster and find change and growth, but I was simply missing the skills needed to evolve in that way.

THE FORGIVENESS

It has been 34 years since I saw the inside of a dumpster; a lot has changed. Thank god for my view from the bottom of a dumpster, it gave me humility, resilience, connection, motivation, and most of all, determination and grit.

I don't expect to ever completely understand why, but I know the experiences and lessons given to me, some more painful than others, directed me to where I am now. One might say it's been a slow trickle and many years of looking for what worked for me to allow happiness in and heal from years of self-sabotage and fear. It was then that I learned to embrace my unique self and was able to wholeheartedly forgive him, and most importantly, wholeheartedly forgive myself.

"Forgiveness frees us from the past and opens energetic space for us to create a better future"

– Debra L. Reble, Ph.D.

THE SPACE

Space, the area in between all objects and thoughts, is where the magic happens, where all things are possible, and where we find connection with ourselves at the deepest level. Forgiveness helped me find the space where I learned that:

- Words matter. Words really matter. I didn't always have the right language to express how words influenced or affected me, and his final words to me took space and time to process and forgive. But his words sparked something deep inside me, and years later, his words created a realization that "sticks and stones will break your bones, but words will never hurt me" is a load of crap.

- Integrity, honesty, and kindness of our words define who we are. That matters, period. You can change your internal landscape with the words you share with yourself. Create a sacred space within you. The bottom of that dumpster was an opportunity filled with gratitude, resilience, determination, and grit.

- Reflection offers powerful truths. How others treat you is not a reflection of who you are, it's a reflection of them. His words showed his burdens, reflection, and trauma to work through. This took me a long time to accept, as it's equally true how I treated others reflected me. *Ouch.*

- This was, at times, an uncomfortable awareness, something not easy to own. For many years my unhealed self projected my internal hurt, fear, and unkindness on others. The universe gifts us limitless opportunities to evolve and shift, but I often chose to be guarded and defensive, shielding my pain from others' view. To all those I treated unfairly, know it was not about you; I had my own healing and learning to do. *I am sorry.*

- Listening deeply holds answers. In the space between the noise, in that space of silence, or when you think life is closing doors on you, the universe is offering you exactly what you need and supportive guidance; always listen deeply.

- In the bottom of the dumpster, when I was hungry and afraid to be seen, I couldn't hear the message, but I now know if I could go back and have the skills to listen, I would have heard: *This is how I am showing you how to rise strong, dig deep, be creative, and curious, develop deep compassion, and live up to your purpose of being in service to guide others.*

THE TOOL

THE COMPREHENSIVE WELLNESS TOOLKIT

Pain, setbacks, and trauma are guarantees in life, but suffering is a choice, and the choices we make determine how we grow, learn and evolve. My clawing out of dumpsters and my passion for supporting others to do the same for themselves result from my choices. Unique choices that did not come from one canned approach or any one therapist, experience, training, retreat, coach, or doctor.

The nonlinear gift of life experiences, multiple steps backward and forward, stops and starts, and repeating the same mistakes, is twisted and messy. As my life coach shared with me, "Colleen, your life is an English garden, yes it's messy, but oh, it is so beautiful." She is so right, and I love my magnificently messy garden!

For years, fear, scarcity, abandonment, and victimization occupied the space now filled with awareness of how I arrived here at wholeness and happiness. It wasn't always easy, but I chipped away at the stories and emotions to re-write my story and honor all my spaces, mind, body, and soul. Because it's at that intersection that magic grows.

Happiness is your divine right; I wish it for you.

Building a personal wellness toolkit requires reflection, listening, and understanding your unique needs. The key is to start practicing. Practice makes better practice. I invite you to decide to get started creating your wellness toolkit, make a subtle shift, and create the approach that supports you.

Here are a few steps to get started.

GO EASY WITH YOURSELF

Breathe in; breathe out. Slow down and begin to feel into your body and the space you are in right now. Simply breathe in; breathe out.

This is not a race, so invite in the idea and trust that you are enough, complete, and whole exactly as you are.

Because if you have come this far in the chapter, you're ready to shift your limiting beliefs, reclaim your sense of self, own and define your purpose, and live with less stress in your life. You realize that pushing harder, pushing past, pushing down, pushing through, and pushing away is not creating the results you want. So, shift the need to push and go easy with yourself. It's a powerful tool.

I invite you to listen to the words, expectations, and thoughts you have toward yourself each day. Each cell in our body is like a mini-brain. They listen to our words and actions, soaking them up like a sponge—positive and negative—and disperse them through your mind and body.

To practice going easy with yourself, try one of these ideas each day:

- Take five minutes each day to do less. Don't fret; less is not nothing; less, in this case, is a lot more and allows you to pause to see what's most important.
- Practice doing one thing at a time. That may be sitting down to eat and simply eating, going for a walk without talking on the phone, or having a conversation on the phone without doing the laundry. Enjoy the moment you are in!

- Catch yourself when you hear yourself judging or speaking unkindly to yourself. Then ask yourself, "What would I say to my best friend in this situation?" Then say it to yourself!
- Take the time to transition between activities. Sum up what you completed and gather your inner resources before you shift into the next task.

This list is far from inclusive, so I invite you to pause and write down your unique list. What steps can you integrate that invite in the idea of ease? Borrow some of mine or create your own and invite the subtle shifts to create ripples of wholeness and wellness through your mind and body.

Everyone has a dumpster full of garbage they're working on, but at this moment, you can decide to go easier with yourself and take inventory of what you do have that can create impactful shifts.

CELEBRATE WHAT YOU HAVE

You were born with all the tools you need to live a balanced and joyful life. However, most of us have lost track, misplaced, or given away our tools. So, to build your wellness toolkit, remind yourself, dust off, and reclaim the strengths you already own. We have all lent a neighbor a ladder, coffee pot, folding table, and then when you need it, you can't find it or have to go get a new one.

Well, this is the time to get your tools in order.

- Where are you giving away time to others when you need time to get your own things done?
- Where is saying yes getting in the way of your exercise time?
- How much time scrolling and comparing to others is pulling your mind and energy away from making a healthy lunch?
- What excuses are you making that prevent you from starting a meditation practice for five minutes each morning?

Whether you realize it or not, you are trading this time and space against your wellness toolkit. I invite you to find one or two areas you can reclaim and shift.

Try this practice. Grab a piece of paper and label five columns with these wellness toolkit components:

- Nourishment
- Emotional Wellbeing
- Physical Movement
- Mindfulness and Meditation
- Connection with Nature

For each, list the strengths and tools you have in each column. Considering how your mind, body, and soul are intertwined, it's normal that some of your tools may fit in multiple categories. Under "Nourishment," you may list healthy snacking habits, good sleeping habits, or the use of essential oils to help energize you. You may list your daily dog walking under "Physical Movement" and "Emotional Health." Be creative, and keep adding until it feels complete.

Of course, the list of tools may change because you are constantly changing, as is the world around you. Embrace this as a practice, and revisit this list and modify it as you grow and shifts happen.

Now you have dusted off your tools and reminded yourself of your strengths, spend time practicing them, catching yourself when you use them, and leaning into them when you find yourself going hard on yourself. Give yourself some credit for showing up each day and doing your best! And as my son reminds me, "Gratitude is the best attitude." Be grateful for what you have.

TAKE A PAUSE

A brief, mindful pause creates space you need to explore your gifts and release what has been getting in the way of what you know you need and will support you.

I invite you to add this brief meditation to your toolkit.

- Find a place to sit, close your eyes or take a gentle gaze, and allow yourself to be still.

- Notice your body breathing for you—what a gift. Allow your mind and body to take in these few moments of pause. Nowhere to be; nothing to do.
- Simply observing your breath, in and out, in and out.
- For one minute, gently repeat to yourself:

  - At this moment, I have everything I need; I go easy with myself.

- When you feel complete, release your repetition, take a few deep breaths, slowly open your eyes.
- Smile and begin your daily activities.

EXPAND YOUR TOOLKIT

Life is not a one-tool kind of job; there will be times when you use one tool more than others, times where you need to create a new tool, and times when you realize an old tool needs to be dusted off to get the job done. Normal daily activities, seasonal changes, different times of your life, and different times of day impact what tools you need to achieve wellbeing and balance. What works for someone may not work for another. Just like some people like spicy food and others do not, there is no right or wrong tool, just the ones that support your unique wellness.

I suggest you start with going easy with yourself and embracing the tools you have. The less you push, turn up the volume on honoring yourself, and trust you have all you need, the closer you move to the balance and wholeness you deserve.

If getting started or staying accountable is challenging, I would be honored to support your progress toward a healthier life. If you are feeling pulled to make real lifestyle shifts so you can fall in love with your life, I am here to help, please reach out.

Set up a free consult with me on my website at www.subtle-shifts.com. Download the complete steps for creating your wellness toolkit at www.subtle-shifts.com/wellnesstoolkit.

I would be honored to support you.

"It is never too late to reclaim the connection to yourself and your true purpose, happiness and balance are obtainable, and you deserve it!"

Colleen is passionate about supporting others in their journey to feel their best and live a harmonious and balanced life. A certified Chopra Integrative Life Coach, Ayurveda Health and Mindfulness Mentor, and Yoga Instructor, her approach embraces the whole person and believes all our spaces - mind, body, and dwelling spaces - are beautifully intertwined.

Colleen co-creates with and guides her clients toward wholeness and purpose; while untangling limiting beliefs, unhealthy patterns, and unconscious conditions.

Her clients say working with Colleen feels like finding themselves again and helps them see they are not their stories, and obstacles once viewed with frustration, fear, and disappointment offer opportunities that guide their transformation.

It all starts with meeting clients where they are now and knowing that subtle shifts create impactful and sustainable transformation. Everyone is unique, and building their wellness toolkit is at the core of her approach and proven through her personal and clients' experiences.

Her approach is holistic, unique, non-judgmental, and offers an informed perspective. Colleen knows her most powerful tools are the ones she has integrated into her life over the last decade by transforming through her own experiences and openly bringing her life lessons, struggles, and transformative tools to her clients.

In addition to her Chopra certifications, Colleen is an Integrative NLP Practitioner, interior designer, and Co-Founder of Tree Sisters.

Find and follow Colleen here:

www.subtle-shifts.com

Instagram: @colleen_avis_bewell

Facebook: www.facebook.com/colleen.avis

CHAPTER 2

THE ART AND SCIENCE OF MANIFESTATION

CREATING YOUR DREAM LIFE

Lisa Vrancken

We've all heard the expression "life is a journey." I believe there are many journeys experienced in one lifetime. Some tend to think life is happening to them. But as the question goes, "what if life is happening *for* you?"

MY STORY

The bluebirds chirped as the sky blushed rose, softly cooing day into night. As usual, residents and tourists began to flock to the Cabin in the Pines, ready to dine at the town's favorite establishment.

The bar and restaurant was owned by my father. It was a popular spot, only miles from Lake George in upstate New York. Nestled in the trees, we lived and worked there, five hours from Brooklyn, where I was born four years earlier.

At night and on weekends, my mother Rose served food, my brother Robert worked the bar, and my sister Frances washed dishes. I was too young, so I was told to sit on a chair and keep my sister company at the industrial sink.

As I got older, my chores were assigned. Each member of the family contributed to the restaurant—that was the deal. We had to earn our keep, as my father would say.

It was a busy dinner, like most. Patrons smiled, smoking cigarettes and sipping cocktails. The pinball machine whirred, and the pool table clacked. Smoky air wafted up the stairs, where we'd sleep after we closed.

What most of the patrons didn't know was that my father was a raging and violent alcoholic. On this particular night, he knocked back vodka after vodka, and the rush went by fast.

After everyone left, my mother ran a hot bath to soothe her aching back. My siblings and I were getting ready for bed. In the distance, I heard my father snarl. I oriented myself. It came from downstairs, in the storeroom, and it was getting louder.

The stale, rotten smell of rage filled the second-floor apartment. His boots made a heavy, dull thud as he hurled himself up the stairs. In an instant, I knew it would be another night of terror.

We scurried. I hid in the closet, hand-in-hand with Frances, peeking through the door.

"You're all pieces of shit," he spat, like venom. "You'll never amount to anything."

His skin flushed red. Tiny molecules of sweat pooled on his forehead. He took the last sip of a bottle and discarded it behind him. The ethanol boiled like fire on his breath.

Tired and worn, my mother folded into herself. The strike happened like a flash. Before she hit the ground, she screamed.

"Go. Run," my brother yelled, distracting my father. The walls shook. The sky thundered against the hillside; we grabbed my mother and ran to the neighbor's house, slogging through mud and rain.

"Oh no!" our neighbor and friend cried out, seeing us distraught, dripping, and shivering in fear. "Come in. Of course, you can stay here. I'll put the girls with my daughter."

That night I may have been saved from one monster, but another lurked in the shadows. The neighbor's daughter Judy and I were best friends. We were both nine years old. Judy's teenage brother, who was just released from reform school, would later sexually abuse his half-sister and me. Another nightmare behind closed doors.

Months passed, and it continued with no end in sight.

At this time, the best thing in my life was Simon, my wild pinto stallion with big, beautiful patches of black and white. Whenever we could escape, I'd jump on his back and ride into the forest.

I'd lay in the field of flowers, wholeheartedly knowing my family deserved so much better. Away from the chaos, I'd start to imagine a life without my father, separate from this godforsaken town. In the solace of nature, I found peace, tranquility, and the ability to focus.

I saw Brooklyn. I saw the smiling faces of my mother's siblings, cousins, and extended family. I pictured a safe home filled with tenderness and joy.

The visions I conjured filled my heart. I had unwavering faith, even when it felt like there was no way out. For the next four years, I'd affirm it. I called to mind my new life every single day.

One day, after I turned thirteen, my mother found the courage.

"I'm ready," she said with conviction. "It's time."

We packed a single bag and never looked back.

"Lord, thank you for our blessings," my mother whispered, floating over the first feast she cooked in our new apartment in the city. My sister had finished high school, and my brother was now a husband, living with his wife. We bowed our heads in grace, emanating love. She lifted the cloth to reveal a basket of warm bread.

I reached my hand past the garlic bread to get a hearty scoop of pasta. I looked up, surrounded by family. *Home*, I thought, *finally*.

***

A shake-up is another kind of blessing. It was in my third year of law school when I had an epiphany—I was 27 and on the wrong path.

I studied political science as an undergrad and interned on The Hill under Geraldine Ferraro, the first female V.P. democratic candidate in U.S. history. I had spent the law school years interning with the ACLU at the height of the AIDS crisis and at one of the largest sex discrimination firms in the country. I aspired to get my J.D. and make real change.

Unfortunately, I saw firsthand the pervasive corruption and inequities of the judicial system. In my gut, I knew I needed to pivot. I bowed out and left the city, searching for purpose. First, I found my way to family.

I visited my brother at his new home in Cornwall-on-Hudson. Recently absconded from the routine lifestyle of a law student, I started dreaming of a life away from the cement jungle. I remembered the feeling of being in nature, and I began to picture my own home by the Hudson River, where I could live and help women in need.

During the visit, my sister-in-law, Sherrie, took me for a tour of the area. Up the road, I saw something out of the corner of my eye. I did a double-take. It was an 1830s Greek Revival that looked like Tara in *Gone With the Wind*—after the war.

"Sherrie, pull over," I blurted, gesturing toward the aging structure.

The home was in a state of disrepair. And yet, something drew me to it. I was mesmerized. I walked up the rickety stairs to knock on the door. No answer. I heard someone mowing their lawn nearby. I approached, unable to contain my excitement.

"Sorry to bother you. Can you tell me anything about this home?" The neighbor, looking perplexed, nodded.

"An elderly recluse named Dr. Richard Smith lives in the house and has a lifetime tenancy," he said. "He's very private and normally doesn't answer the door."

I couldn't stop thinking about the house; I felt like it was calling me. The dreams continued. I visualized myself there. I saw how I'd inhabit the rooms and decorate the walls. It would be my home, my sacred space, and maybe one day, a holistic center for healing.

I followed my intuition and drove back to the house a week later. This time, I knocked on the door, believing it would open. When the 87-year-old doctor answered, it was the beginning of a profoundly enriching journey for both of us.

We spent the next year and a half developing a connection on a deep spiritual level. He was like a father to me, acknowledging my light and encouraging me to see myself as I never had before.

"You're beyond special, and you have so much to give to the world," he said. "Share your gifts."

Dr. Smith arranged for me to purchase the home and become the new owner at the time of his passing. I thrived.

During the day, I busted my ass, working to be able to pay the bills and begin the restoration. At night, I engaged in the study of major religions, quantum physics, brainwaves, and the power of the mind.

I became an avid reader, voraciously consuming books on a variety of subjects. I learned different forms of meditation and mindfulness practices. I received certifications in biofeedback, hypnotherapy, and neuro-linguistic programming (NLP), which I used to reprogram my psyche and heal my relationship with pain from the past.

My definitions of home and family shifted. I rebuilt the house—and myself—at the same time.

***

Years later, I found my voice in the world of video. I moved to Delray Beach, Florida, to be closer to my mother, who remarried a loving doctor.

Life has a way of taking you in unexpected directions. I became an award-winning T.V. producer, global product strategist, and marketing consultant. I was busy telling stories, producing videos, and building company brands. As a passion project, I decided to create a mini-documentary on the topic of childhood sexual abuse called *Raising Humanity*, earning me a Silver Telly Award as the Executive Producer.

Out of nowhere, I had an appendicitis attack and was rushed to the emergency room. Standard testing revealed a bigger problem: a grapefruit-size tumor between my heart and lungs. I was later diagnosed with Hodgkin's Lymphoma.

I had a good cry, but not for long.

Every day, I visualized myself as healthy. I'd look in the mirror and repeat aloud: "Lisa, you're full of vim and vigor. You're already healed."

Consistently, I did my morning rituals. I spent time with energetic healers. I had a cocktail of chemotherapy and ultimately decided against radiation. I ate quality food, and I exercised. I believed all would be well, and my belief was strong.

My surgeon and his team were angels sent from heaven. Everything went smoothly, and it was a success.

Eleven years later, I'm still in remission and feeling unstoppable.

***

I'm living proof that manifestation is available to everyone. If you focus your whole being on something, you can make it a reality. We all have the power, and our personal experiences are just a part of our unique puzzle.

I'm one of the countless children who grew up with an alcoholic parent or survived childhood sexual abuse. Many of us have our own war stories, and I share mine, so others don't feel alone. We no longer need to hide what we've been through because we can learn to channel it.

I shifted my kaleidoscope yet again, and a new vision started to come into focus. I believe my personal mission is to mentor individuals from all walks of life to stand in their power, and I saw myself providing the tools and frameworks to help women uncover and communicate their truths.

My passion expanded and evolved. I started to journal my thoughts on how I could interweave everything I'd learned into a book that would reach the people who really needed it.

It didn't take long for Ashley Black and Korie Minkus to enter my life through a series of seemingly cosmic introductions.

From our first meeting, we appreciated each other's unique talents and gifts. Ashley Black is the inventor of the FasciaBlaster® tools with more than fifty patents, and she currently owns one of the fastest-growing nine-figure private companies in America. Korie Minkus is the founder and CEO of Rock Your Product, a brilliant global brand strategist, and consultant with over a billion dollars in retail sales.

Together, we're creating BE...*From Passion and Purpose to Product and Prosperity*. Our book is a shared vision with pearls of wisdom for personal development, self-transformation, and a deep activation of the female entrepreneurial spirit. It's currently available for pre-order at https://www.amazon.com/dp/1642937886/.

Through manifestation, I found my perfect co-authors. Written for women by women, *BE...*is not your ordinary business book. We've woven holistic principles of self-discovery with proven proprietary business philosophies and product-to-market systems.

During our writing collaboration, we devoted our time to building a relationship with an audience of women. We created a private Facebook group named "The Writing of the Book," where we host weekly Thursday night Facebook Live events (our version of a weekly podcast).

No matter where you come from and no matter where you're at, we all seek the same thing—to live a life of passion and purpose that sets our souls on fire.

It's true that living in a dysfunctional environment in my early years made me vulnerable to abuse, but I'm no longer ashamed. I've walked through some dark alleys. I spent time in toxic relationships that didn't serve me. I had money, and then I didn't. I was healthy, and then I wasn't. But every time I was broken, I visualized. I healed, and it has made me the strong, determined, compassionate, successful woman I am today.

Through it all, I never let myself get stuck. I never stopped believing. I mean, how could I? I'm a manifestor.

As it's been said, "I will attract what I am, and what we all are is energy and vibration."

THE TOOL

"Where awareness goes, energy flows." Though it's only five words, the famed saying refers to an unexplainable phenomenon and a rule rooted in the study of physics. And that's exactly why manifestation truly is both an art and a science.

In psychology, manifestation is defined as "using our thoughts, feelings, and beliefs to bring an idea into our physical reality." At a young age, I intuitively knew that by focusing on my imaginings, I could make them real. The basics, believing everything we need is inside of us, and we alone have the power to create our life, came easy to me. What I needed to learn was two things: personal practice and patience.

First, we must recognize the principle that everything within our reality—every action, thought, and emotion—is a frequency. Each of us is constantly moving through a field of vibration, where all possibility exists.

To create the life of your dreams, you must believe in endless possibilities. Endless good. Endless love. Because manifestation is more than willing what you want into existence, it's alchemical magic of thoughts, speech, feelings, and most importantly, actions. Here are the top tenets of my practice to achieve the desired outcome.

RELEASE LIMITING BELIEFS

The words, thoughts, and frequencies we emit to the universe influence what we receive. Harmful limiting beliefs, carried like an invisible weight in the subconscious, can sabotage our lives. I know because memories laced with negativity haunted me for years.

Developing from the womb to age seven, limiting beliefs are formative imprints that shape our perceptions. They're the negative thoughts and feelings we have about ourselves and the world. It's our self-talk, our mind chatter.

Thinking negative thoughts attracts more of the same. It's an energetic self-fulfilling prophecy; it becomes a feedback loop that causes doubt, keeps us in victim mode, and blocks our manifestation.

Drop that bitchy voice who tells you, "I can't." Don't allow thoughts like "I'm not worthy" to take up space in your mind. If you find yourself thinking anything close to "I'm not enough," hit the eject button.

Go within. Identify. Release.

Rinse and *repeat.*

MEDITATE AND CONNECT WITH SOURCE

Beyond energy is the concept of Source. Is it God, Spirit, Universe, the All-knowing? Whatever name you fancy works for me. The important thing is tapping into the idea of a higher power.

The Source flows through all life. It's energy, and it's everywhere and within us. By entering a meditative state, you can become aligned with the Source of ultimate power. You can then change your brainwave frequency, build resistance to stress, and rebalance your nervous system.

When negative thoughts enter like unwelcome guests, you can direct them to exit, letting the positive energy of Source move through you.

The universe is conspiring to support us, and we must meet it with openness and faith. Connect with Source to connect with Self.

AFFIRMATIONS, JOURNALING, AND VISION BOARDS

Affirmations are daily phrases used to create focus and presence, allowing you to become consciously intentional with your thoughts. The universe and the quantum world are mathematical. I like to affirm on a numerical schedule—using the divine numbers discussed by Nicola Tesla, the Serbian-American inventor, engineer, and physicist.

The Divine numbers are three, six, and nine. Here's how I learned it: when I desire to manifest an idea into reality, I journal three affirmations. I review those affirmations six times a day to get on a continuous frequency, which allows me to stay in alignment with the vibration. I focus my energy for nine seconds on each affirmation, for a total of 27 seconds. It's a short amount of time for something that could mean so much.

Visual affirmations help too. Take pictures or collect photos from magazines that you can place on a board to remember the life you desire. It can be pictures of your dream business, career, home, or car, a vision of a healthier body, the fashion and accessories you'd like to wear, destinations you'd like to travel and food you'd love to eat, and hobbies you'd love to learn, or service and charities that you want to support. Go further than materialistic desires to include all areas of life.

Say, write, and allow yourself to see what you want in specific detail. Give a date as to when you want to bring it into reality, and be patient.

LOVING-KINDNESS, SERVICE, AND GRATITUDE

Lastly, being heart-centered matters. When I manifest, I think about how I can give to others from my heart. It raises the consciousness of love and superpowers your manifestation.

During and after manifesting, practice gratitude to complete your process.

Repeat, repeat, repeat, and never give up.

Lisa Vrancken is the Executive Vice President at Fortune Media Group, a media company breaking barriers and redefining the art of commercials and corporate videos. She works directly with Kevin Harrington, the original shark of Shark Tank.

An award-winning T.V. producer and media expert, Lisa has spent decades artfully and strategically creating brand awareness and driving revenue. She's also the creator of Innovator's Think Tank, a globally-attended quarterly event for product innovators. She's worked with everyone, from local start-ups to large-scale international entrepreneurs.

Lisa is a co-author of *BE...From Passion and Purpose to Product and Prosperity* with Ashley Black and Korie Minkus. Distributed by Simon & Schuster, it's currently on pre-sale at all fine bookstores.

During the writing of the book in 2020, Lisa formed BE...PPPP, LLC with co-authors Ashley Black and Korie Minkus. There are so many women looking for guidance, support, and someone to believe in their dreams, and that's the exact mission and the philosophy of the BE...Movement.

BE...PPPP, LLC was designed for our community, united together to create prosperity. We'll offer self-transformational gatherings and professional masterminds for women in entrepreneurship through retreats to Costa Rica and other exotic locations around the globe in 2022.

Connect with Lisa at https://fortunemediagroupinc.com/

Find her private group on Facebook, The Writing of the Book, here: https://www.facebook.com/groups/199541728147867

CHAPTER 3

BREATHWORK

FROM STRESSED TO CONSCIOUS AND FREE

Tanya Saunders

"You entered on an inhale and will exit this life on an exhale."

—anonymous

MY STORY

I survived the flesh-eating bacteria. Every morning I'm reminded of that as I stare at the reflection of battle scars mid-forearm to triceps, with thick suture lines from a skin graft that covered what was once a gaping hole on my elbow. This is the image reflected back to me every morning as I self-consciously blow-dry my hair and think, *dang, that's fugly*. I shouldn't need a mantra or positive affirmation on a Post-It note to remind me of how powerful I am and how fragile life really is when I have that visual plugged in on repeat into my morning routine.

It had been a decade since, and I was still living in hustle mode. Was I really waiting for another rock bottom moment and life-threatening experience to finally wake up to awareness and mindfulness?

I was a victim of the have-do-be syndrome. I wanted to have, to feel, to then be. I also chose to plant roots with three kids where 2000 square foot houses are more than half a million dollars, further capitulating me to the rat race of a woman who dreamed of manifesting a *full* life.

"I'll retire you in three years," I told my husband in 2017 when I launched my first small business while still working full-time as a nurse anesthetist. Until then, I was thinking, *I'll continue to work out every morning at zero dark thirty, sandwich 40 hours into three shifts at the hospital, play Uber driver to the kids in the evenings, soccer mom on the weekends, and plug-in Wednesday date nights with my husband to be 'that' woman.*

It wasn't until after I found breathwork that the mud of having first to have, to feel, to be was wiped from my lens of rose-colored realism.

THE BREATHWORK JOURNEY

"Wow, something happened to you." My gaze floated to the yoga mat beside me as another student touched me. I was slowly coming back to planet Earth from my first breathwork journey. My hair was wet, the backside of my sleeveless top was soaked with a mixture of warm and cold. I sat up. *WTF happened. I just time and space traveled. I took a journey into my unconscious.*

My current sweaty mess situation took me back to the room labeled "Contact Isolation" and flooded me with memories of a week, waking up night after night, hospital gown soaked, sheets drenched, as my body was releasing the toxins from the flesh-eating bacteria that violated my arm and was like venom in my blood. It reminded me of the uncomfortable feelings of fear, shame, sadness, and so much regret that filled my body about things I had done and had not done yet. *I'm not ready to die.*

I was settling into a more alert state. I'm no virgin to alcohol, but I imagine my experience is what taking any psychedelic or a powerful plant medicine would be like; a journey into another dimension in hopes to reconnect to nature and our true selves. *Wowser, this is amazing.* I didn't need to go to Peru for an Ayahuasca retreat to heal childhood baggage when I just experienced this. I felt light and spacious inside, like I was floating in a five-dimensional world, with no care, no attachment, simply peace. *This is bliss.*

My gaze came into focus and locked on the other student. I was in San Diego for a five-day immersion of a seven-month Pause Breathwork facilitator course I impulsively but intuitively embarked on.

A MONTH BEFORE

"Can you call me?"

"Hey babe, I know it may not make sense, but I need you to support me." A rare call, not a text. Seconds ago, his patient's heart rate was faint; now I could really hear it, *or is that mine starting to speed up?* In my mind's eye, I saw the shallow rising and falling of my husband's scrub top as he whispered, "okay." It had been 18 years, and he was accustomed to my brain and soul-feeding ideas.

I thought about a life coaching certification to support the lifestyle entrepreneurship I kicked off in 2017, but one humid August evening in DC and one life-changing random email was all it took for a fork in the road. A beta Breathwork Certification. *Breathwork, what the?*

As a nurse anesthetist, I was in control of breathing patients for two decades. Pressure control/volume guarantee, *check*, respiratory rate ten, *check*, inspiration/expiration ratio 1:2, *check*. I never understood our breath as a lost art and science, not just for stress relief but also as a transformative tool and healing modality.

Yet it is.

I experienced one of those confusing psychological concepts. The unconscious is what Freud said is below the tip of the iceberg. It's the most important part of the mind, and it powerfully influences our thoughts, feelings, actions, and our results in our life.

It's what Swiss psychologist Carl Jung coined "shadows," those parts of ourselves we deem unworthy, and we disown.

It's what Debbie Ford described as the locked doors in our castle. You're born a magnificent castle, mystical and magical, with long hallways of thousands of rooms. But with every visitor, day after day and year after year in our castle, the doors to rooms are locked and forgotten as visitors tell you your castle would be perfect without this room, that room, and the room over there.

EMOTIONAL NEEDS

We live in an emotionally constipated world.

Tanya, why are you angry? You should be grateful you didn't die. Tanya, why do you care so much about that scar? You should be grateful you didn't lose your arm. You caused this; maybe God was punishing you because you dream too big. Let it go; you have too many goals. Are you still upset because your mom worked nights and couldn't help you with your hair before school? Are you embarrassed about your roots that you feel you have to accomplish your self-worth? Are you still feeling that shame about failing your first nursing boards? Focus on your family; they should be your first priority, not work, your body, workouts, the way your house looks, the clothes you wear.

We all have natural human needs: love, acceptance, safety, connection, and purpose, to name a few. When our human need is not met, they become a wound that hurts. These wounds develop into vulnerable parts when we're young.

It's also natural for humans not to want to feel the pain from the wound. *If my kids wear this outfit and play these sports, they will have these kinds of friends, and their parents will think we are these kinds of people.* We create protectors to try and meet our needs. I was The Addict, addicted to work, hustling for my worth, and trying to "be someone" to be loved on a deeper level.

As adults, we don't have an awareness of the protectors.

It lives in the unconscious.

In our shadows.

In the room with the locked doors.

The breath can illuminate our shadows, unlock the doors, and free the parts that need to be seen and loved. Breath by breath, the conscious breath can travel through our protective layers to bring light, awareness, and compassion to the parts we have separated from.

WHY BREATHWORK MATTERS TO YOU

Imagining as if I was truly floating above my body during my first meditative breathwork journey, I would see my breath quiet my mind and start to relax my nervous system and slow my brain waves down. *How long is this going to take? Breathwork is like a workout. I wonder what my husband is thinking? Did I remember to coordinate that carpool? What do my friends think of me leaving my kids for five days? San Diego is amazing, and I want to live in wine country. I need to vacation more. I need to make more money first.*

This chatter is the mind's work. Our mind is the mental activity of the brain and is designed to keep us safe. Modern science has proven that most mental activity, our thinking mind, is negative and repetitive. And because our mind is built to keep us safe, unless we bring intentional awareness to our thoughts, we continue the same cycle, the same thinking, the same life, day after day.

The power of breathwork is we surrender the mind, not by thinking, trying, and forcing, but by focusing our attention on the breath.

Five to seven minutes more into breathing, *my feet and lips are tingling, I'm kinda cold. What is happening to my body?* Ten minutes and more, I have shifted into the rest/digest/create parasympathetic nervous system, and I'm in a place now where there lives a possibility of my breath unlocking the doors and freeing my fears in my emotional needs of validation, belonging, community, purpose.

You have the ability to bypass the thinking mind, which is the biggest block to awareness, feeling our feelings, and ultimately to healing.

BREATHWORK

Breathing is automatic, just like our heartbeat. Yet, it's the only part of our autonomic nervous system we can control without any medicine or technology.

Expert Dan Brule defines breathwork as "the art and science of using breath awareness and breathing exercises for health, growth, and change in body, mind, and spirit."

As a Pause Breathwork Facilitator, I guide in integrative methods designed to be used moment to moment in our waking life when you need to take a breather. *Can't my husband make dinner? I can't find my keys; the dog got into the trash again; why are there socks everywhere, stop the electronics, do you not know how to put the dishes into the sink or in the dishwasher, oh my God, the emails.*

I also guide in Meditative Breathwork with the intention of an altered state of consciousness promoting the deepest self-healing and personal transformation. *Is this what Buddha meant by pure awareness and non-attachment?*

Breath is the foundation of our life force. It's also a need, not a want for our vitality, yet most humans don't tap into the capacity nor the link of our breath to our emotional, mental, and physical well-being.

Used safely and intentionally, your breath becomes a superhero's secret weapon to kryptonite, the unconscious mind.

THE TOOL

WHAT YOU NEED TO KNOW BEFORE YOU BREATHE

As you intentionally breathe and move energy over a sustained period of time, physiologic changes occur in blood pH, a state called respiratory alkalosis. This shift occurs as you inhale more oxygen and exhale more carbon dioxide. This is not hyperventilation as in a panic attack where the breath is shallow, rapid, chaotic, and without intention (see common physiologic sensations).

Every emotion has a corresponding breath pattern. Shallow chest breathing is generally connected to stress, and slow, deep belly breaths are connected to safety and calm. As you intentionally breathe, emotional sensations may occur (see common emotional sensations).

Although breathwork slows the thinking mind, it's not a mind healing modality. Breathwork is a body healing modality. Emotions that have been resisted, ignored, and buried may surface. The body releases whatever it needs to release. The body becomes the healer.

Every breathwork experience will be different. I'd advise having a trained breathwork facilitator to safely guide you through an experience longer than eight minutes. It's important to know that you are of the highest authority and are in control of your breath at all times. As one of the eight attitudes of mindfulness, I invite you to have a beginner's mind, be open and curious about the power of your breath in releasing the stress, emotions that are stuck and want to be felt. Releasing the stress in your body with breathwork unlocks the more conscious and freer version of you.

Finally, you are breathing energy, not air. Breathwork is safe.

It's safe to breathe.

It's safe to feel.

It's safe to be in your body.

It's safe to be aware.

It's safe to be free.

Potential Physical Sensations (normal physical sensations that can occur as you breathe).

- Lightheadedness
- Tingling
- Pressure
- Pain (trapped energy)
- Urges to move
- Urges to make sound
- Sexual energy
- Sensual responses
- Cramping
- Temperature shifts

Potential Emotional Sensations (normal emotional sensations that can occur as you breathe).

- Sadness
- Joy
- Inspiration
- Awakening
- Rage
- Anger
- Frustration
- Surprise

Integrative Breathwork (Take a breather three to eight minutes)

POSTURE

Integrative breathwork can be done sitting or lying but not driving. I think of my body as an antenna connecting my human nature to the Divine source. Find a posture that is supportive in a feeling of grounded, plugged in, alert, open, receptive, and connected. *Are my feet flat on the ground if possible, spine straight, shoulders dropped, wide and relaxed? Eyes closed or with a soft gaze, jaw loose, crown of my head reaching to the sky. Am I rooting to rise?*

INTENTION

Other than the breath, the intention is everything in breathwork. How do you want to feel? Get clear and decide on the desired outcome. *I would love to feel like a better mom. I would love to feel more loved. I would love to feel like a confident leader. I want to feel less anxious. I would love to feel more appreciated.*

MUSIC

Breathwork can be done without music, but music has an important role in breathwork. Music has a vibration and a frequency. The cadence and rhythm of music have a connection with our emotional states and can enhance the experience and the desired intention. Music helps focus the brain on the task at hand. Slower beats per minute (BPM) are more inviting, and grounding and higher BPMs are more excitable, activating, and have a higher pain threshold. *Wow, this song by Beautiful Chorus was written for me.*

MANTRA

Mantras are words that have the immense power to transform your life. A mantra repeated over and over is a subtle process of influencing consciousness. The word MANTRA comes from two root words: 1. MAN = manas, mind 2. TRA = tool, instrument. It's a tool to train the mind. When a mantra is intentionally chosen, used silently or out loud during breathwork, it has the ability to help alter the limiting beliefs that are in our subconscious. Mantras are used more commonly as positive affirmations in the western world, and the words have a vibration and frequency to transform the nature of the mind and thought forms. *I am powerful. Money flows easily to me. I am abundant. It's safe to let go and release.*

Breathwork for Anxiety (three to eight minutes)

Inhale through the nose at a count of four, and longer exhale through the mouth at a count of six.

Breathwork for Anger (three to eight minutes)

Inhale through the nose at a count of four and exhale with an audible sound like a sigh or scream.

Breathwork for Power (three to eight minutes)

Inhale through the nose at a count of six and exhale through the mouth at a count of four.

Breathwork for Balance (three to eight minutes)

Inhale through the nose at a count of four, pause at a count of four, exhale through the nose at a count of four, pause for a count of four.

Breathwork for Love (six minutes)

Inhale through the nose for a count of six, exhale through the mouth for a count of six.

Breathwork for Transformation (Greater than eight minutes of continual conscious breathing)

Increased awareness and mind-body-soul connection will naturally occur over sustained and devoted Integrative breathwork practices on your own. Meditative breathwork for a quantum leap of transformation is advised with a certified trauma-informed breathwork facilitator.

INTROSPECTION

The breath can pierce through the protective armor humans have put on to shield themselves from the pain of the past and fear of the future. Therefore the protective armor has become the costume of us acting to protect our tender hearts from disappointment, failures, and the stress that have muddied the path to our true needs and our true self. The breath can guide you back home, where you don't have to have, to do, to be. You have everything you already need inside of you. You have permission now to just be.

Tanya Saunders is a Certified Life Mastery Consultant, Trauma-Informed Pause Breathwork Facilitator, Yoga Psychology Teacher, Expert Transformation & Manifestation Speaker, and intern to Astrology. A survivor of a life-threatening condition, necrotizing fasciitis in 2009, she is passionate about cultivating a vision-inspired life and helping working women live a harmonious life through breath, positive neuroplasticity, and astrology.

She is the creator of The HEALthy Mind Podcast and HEAlthy Mind coaching, a framework of ancient and modern teachings, practices, and wisdom she has invested in and made her own for strengthening the mind-body-soul connection. Integrating this framework into her 1:1 and group coaching, she has helped women discover their true purpose and manifest work/life harmony through soul alignment.

As a Nurse Anesthetist for over two decades, Tanya is always learning new ways to bridge science and art to empower the busy, modern woman who desires to manifest a soul-centered life. She lives in Arlington, VA, with her husband, three kids, and two dogs.

She has been featured on The Beautiful Grit Podcast with Gwen Dittmar, Everything with Ali Levine Podcast, Keri Faith on Purpose, and featured with John Lee Dumas of Entrepreneurs on Fire.

You are one breath away from transformation. Are you ready to go on a Meditative Breathwork Journey? Click here https://onamission.bio/healthymind

CHAPTER 4

PERCEPTION, PERSPECTIVE, AND THE PRACTICE OF PRESENCE

EMPOWERING HEALING THROUGH CONNECTION

Dr. Jill Pierce Beasley, ND, LAc, LMT, RYT

Dear reader,

I want you to read this chapter and feel comfort in the human experience, knowing that there is much to learn through our mortality and even more to learn through our divinity, that those who caused harm taught us something sacred, and that our lifelong journey is to dive into loving connections with ourselves, others, and the world.

Love and light,

Jill

MY STORY

A friend's wise words gave me insight into an important theme in my life:

"One's perception of oneself is just one perception of oneself."

Everything changes—that's the one constant in life. But how many of our ideas are fixed? What constructs limit us and prevent us from experiencing life in a new light? These ideas of perception and perspective give us the framework for how we experience our reality, maybe even our truth. But that can change in an instant.

It's hard to figure out where to begin with this topic. So, I will make it easy. We die. Every human being on this planet will face their physical death and, depending on one's spiritual or religious beliefs, will experience a spiritual transformation. It's the one guarantee in life, the one thing known; yet, mortality is rarely discussed. When someone passes, their loss is mourned, and their life celebrated. Then, the conversation and often the outward expression of emotion is over. Religious traditions refer to heavens and hells and their in-betweens as the eternal afterlife. In some traditions, there is reincarnation and ultimately enlightenment. We are told to have faith in whatever lies beyond this earthly experience, and that is fine, but I want to talk about it. I want to talk about the doubt. I want to talk about the unsettling feeling that drapes me like a dark cloth, the constriction of my throat, and the warm tears that drip down my cheek when I succumb to my extreme fear of death. I know there are no human answers other than to have faith, but I need to explore the depths of the darkness to fully experience all the joy that life has to offer.

The topic of mortality is challenging. Perhaps it is even the root of most fear. There is no way around it, and I hate it, but mortality is something that has loomed over me most of my life. I said that perspective could change instantly, and mine did when I was eight years old.

That's right; I was eight years old when I realized my mortality. *Oh my God, I'm going to die one day.* My chest tightened, and I thought I might suffocate from the feeling of despair and the weight that I now carried. This was my new normal, and my new perception of life, except it wasn't about living. It was all about dying. The innocent joy of childhood was shattered and replaced by a fear of death that would weave its way into my thoughts, behaviors, and decisions daily. I knew I couldn't escape death; I couldn't even escape the thought of death. I was in the third grade. I think it was February. In what seems like one week, my grandmother passed away, a friend died after getting hit by a drunk driver, and my sister was diagnosed with an unpredictable but possibly terminal illness. Bless my little soul; it was too much for her to process.

This new realization took over my life and would forever leave an impact. In the beginning, it was a nightly ordeal. I would get ready for bed, and right before I fell asleep, I would have a moment of awareness of my mortality. It would be brief and as simple as the thought of death, but that would often spiral into the imaginary but crippling and suffocating feeling of the black cloth being draped over me and tightened. Completely overwhelmed, I would sob and seek the solace of my parents, tucked by their sides under the comfort of the sheets and protected from the weight of humanness. I struggled to sleep, quit gymnastics, and clung to my parents' feet before school, begging not to go in fear of my, or their, imminent death. If not daily, this happened weekly, and this is where my journey into breathwork, meditation, and mindfulness began. This was also when routine became a saving grace.

It took about a year of counseling and a consistent nightly routine to get me to the point where I could be social. My dad made me a hot chocolate, tucked me in, and said the Lord's prayer with me every single night until I was thirteen. I started new sports and fell in love with diving. Anxiety and fear still plagued me. The experience of being hyperaware of my mortality didn't go anywhere, but I learned to be present with my fear. It evolved with time, and the looming became less dark. Visualization, mind games of distraction, and focusing on the rise and fall of my breath helped me find enough calm to fall asleep. When my fear first set in, the visualizations were shades of color and unicorns and butterflies. Later on, I tried creating my dreams with anything that kept my mind away from the darkness.

Journaling and reading came into my life next. I read everything and anything—the Bible, the Bhagavad Gita, Thich Nhat Hanh, Thomas Merton, Paulo Coelho, Dante, Socrates, Plato, Kant, Emerson, Jung, James Marion, Ken Wilber, Rudolf Steiner, and so on. I wanted to explore the unknown and understand, or at the very least, find a way to cope with the fear and anxiety. By the time I was a teenager, my relationship with my mortality had started to transform from utter fear into awe of all existence. I wondered about my purpose on earth and my karmic path. I contemplated the vastness of the universe, the uniqueness of people that crossed my path, and the mystery of the human species. I asked a lot of questions. *What are we evolving toward? What higher purpose does humanity serve? Will I have another life on earth?* I didn't know, and I don't know, but I could use my curiosity and logic as a distraction.

My unique awareness of mortality gives meaning to my life. It makes me try harder, care more, and love deeper. It makes me practice presence in discomfort. I am fully aware of the death-rebirth cycle necessary for growth. Just as one's earthly life is marked by birth and death, emotional and spiritual growth is a continual process of shedding one's layers to reveal a lighter, truer self. Often the "death" process, or dark night of the soul, is painful and requires the surrender of our ego, but it awakens the soul to a clearer purpose and shifts one's level of consciousness. This internal process of death and rebirth, for me, is a gesture of life. Perhaps we come to earth as a transition, as a time to grow, learn, and evolve. Perhaps we all have a higher spiritual purpose that is completely unfathomable.

I accept this awareness of mortality as a gift. When it comes at night, it is softer. I still go to my breath. I say a prayer or a mantra. When the fear creeps back in, I greet it, respect it, and settle into a place of belief that my fear and anxiety are limitations and false perceptions. If I am not in true, impending danger, I have the capacity in every moment to shift my thoughts and redirect an experience of existence in real-time. Sometimes I redirect to a place of peace and calm, and sometimes I spiral. I can't always avoid the curiosity of my mind. *If something else exists when we die, will I remember this life? Will I remember the tender moments, the sound of my grandfather's voice and the way his house smelled? Will I remember the last time I held a hand? Will I remember the laughter and tears, the passion and intimacy, and all the moments in between? Or will I just be a soul stripped to its essence, lost in a vortex of souls?* I fear forgetting. Chills run down my spine at the thought of never again seeing the people that have loved and carried me through this life and have brought it meaning.

Mortality is a difficult topic because there is no tangible answer. It will remain an unknown as long as I am in this physical body or until I am enlightened, but I'm fairly certain that won't happen this time around. I think some truths are discoverable, but I'm unsure that a true grasp of life after life is one of them. It baffles me that so many people live with a firm belief about the afterlife. A lot of comforts can be found through dogma, especially around an abstract concept. I often wonder if people with unwavering faith ever lie awake at night questioning what lies beyond. Do they let doubt creep in? Maybe they do, which is why so many people feel threatened by different belief systems and other perspectives. If we accept other people as they are and that their understanding of life may also hold truth, it shatters the concrete barriers of our convictions. As soon as those walls crumble, we get thrown into the abyss of the unknown. This is where fear takes over, comfort disappears, and we are left in a place without an answer. Our mortality confronts us, our faith is challenged, and we are forced to struggle with something for which there may be no answer. We can easily turn back to dogma and dualism, compartmentalizing people and ideas into their appropriate boxes and labels. However, this is a way of living and thinking that doesn't work for me. Give me the unknown, and give me the precious reminder of my mortality. It keeps me honest, and it keeps me searching.

Listen and respond without judgment or expectation—that's my process. Growth and learning on any path, but especially that of a healer, come through the constant shedding of ideas to allow new insights and be open to inspiration. Letting go, the surrender, the metaphorical death, and dissolution create clarity, intimacy with the true self, and the unfolding process of resurrection. Allowing oneself to struggle brings one closer to one's true self, and in that process, meaning and purpose are clarified. And from my perspective, that may just be the meaning of life, at least in this iteration of my understanding.

Without struggle, there is no growth. My struggle with fear has given me the ability to sit with other people in their fear, sadness, anxiety, pain, and darkness. It's a continual practice of being comfortable with the uncomfortable. You can bring your humanness and be held in a sacred space without judgment and from a place of understanding that we are all here, navigating life to the best of our ability.

An experience working with a woman with terminal cancer will stay with me forever. She was a mother with a young child. He was maybe seven years old and would sit in the corner of the room playing during her appointments. It was her eyes that nearly broke me. Glassy from held-back tears, her eyes revealed a distance like her soul was starting to separate from her body. But she held on in desperation, taking long pauses to watch her son play on the concrete floor. I could see the despair, anger, fear, loss, and the knowing that she wouldn't watch her son grow up. I've learned a lot from elderly people and people near their transition out of this earthly realm. I've listened and watched people weep in agony from the fear and others with peace and acceptance. I've heard people's voices in the depths of depression, ready to take their lives, and my role was and will always be a non-judgmental presence. It's not a burden for me to see or hear or feel the weight of being human; it's an honor and reminds me of the interconnectedness of all humanity.

I didn't know those early days of learning to embrace my fear would prepare me to be present with people navigating their struggles. That's the sacredness of my practice—presence in people's willingness to be vulnerable in the sharing of their pain and trust in my guidance. My struggle is my greatest gift and my greatest teacher. Through this ongoing struggle, the willingness to explore the darkness, and the many mentors that challenged my perceptions and taught me new perspectives, my tool of connection began to develop.

Grappling with fear is a necessity in my journey and my commitment to medicine and healing. I haven't conquered fear; I let it transform me by learning to respect it and by living through it, allowing it to let me question my values and my sanity. Through my studies in medicine, massage, and acupuncture, I have the honor to see people's vulnerability and strength and hear their life stories. I continually hone my skills as a healer, but the true healer lies within each person. The art of healing is to be a mirror so that others can see their strength, light, and love and to facilitate an individual in the direction of their goals and healing process.

THE TOOL

Healing is my life's work—understanding the intricacies of human existence as physical, emotional, social, and spiritual interconnectedness.

Most people acknowledge that we are more than mere physical bodies, but how often do we look through a truly holistic framework? We are wired to compartmentalize and reduce most things to the realm of the physical or material world. Even within medicine, we often forget the whole and get trapped in a narrow perspective-isolating a problem to a specific set of muscles or one organ system. We look for one answer when the magic lies in the multitude of questions. It lies in the spaces, the pause, and the uncertainty. We have lost our ability to perceive, and the healer's challenge is to regain that capacity, listen to the subtleties, and learn through curiosity.

When I place my hands on a body, I soften—my hands relax, my shoulders drop, and I feel my breath rise and fall. I slowly allow my hands to sink until the tissue responds. The difference in depth and pressure is subtle, maybe the weight of a feather and the easiest way to describe it is a softening of the hands. Just above the muscles, there is a movement like a winding river. The body is its own guide to unwinding its patterns; my role is to be open enough to listen to that guidance and facilitate the unwinding. Intellect isn't the only or "highest" form of knowledge. If I see only through my intellect, I've limited myself to one perspective and lost the capacity to intuit and connect with deeper ways of knowing.

This idea of meeting applies not only to my hands but also to my heart. In a heart-focused practice, there is an invitation to be present in the healing space. My practice is sacred; the person in front of me is sacred. It's in that connected space, whether through words or bodywork or remedies, that healing is invited in. This is real medicine, and this is what we've lost in our current medical model.

Connection can be as simple as awareness of the breath. That's where I always start and where I always return.

Close your eyes. If you can, lie down and release your body into the ground. Notice the way your breath moves through your body.

Is it smooth and steady, or does it get stuck somewhere in the chest or diaphragm?

Don't judge; just perceive.

Are there sensations of tightness anywhere in the body?

Receive every exhale and allow it to create softness so that the edges of your body begin to blur.

Feel the heaviness of the body and mind sink into the ground.

Notice any emotions. Are they being held anywhere in the body?

Shift your awareness back to your breath.

Feel the subtle movement of the body—with every inhale, follow the wavelike motion to the top of the head and down to the tips of the toes.

On the exhale, feel everything come back to center, still feeling heavy and releasing the body a little more.

Can you feel the connection to the breath, following every rise and fall?

Mind and body unite through the breath to create calm. In this space, perceptions constantly change, and new perspectives are born. In this space, a gift of connection and a sacred pause can be felt. This is medicine.

If I've learned anything in this life and my ongoing practice as a healer, it's that my perspective will continue to evolve as I allow new experiences to transform me. I hope that I'm always open-minded so that my beliefs don't become limiting and that I can see through other lenses, allowing for both simplicity and complexity. Shifting perspectives helps identify obstacles in the healing path and often reveals multifaceted solutions. Bridging ancient healing wisdom with conventional medical knowledge allows me to push the boundaries of my understanding into the unknown. I get to explore the nuances of a person's life—the way that they nourish themselves in body, mind, and spirit; their quantity and quality of sleep; how and how often they move; the way they breathe; their willpower, mindset, resilience, and motivation; the way they interact with themselves and the world; their sense of joy and purpose; their connection with themselves, others, and nature; and how all of these interplay with their ailments and healing process. Together, we find the path toward short and long-term goals and a better quality of life, optimizing living from moment to moment. This is healing; this is wellness; this is only one perspective.

Jill Pierce Beasley is a native of Knoxville, Tennessee, and earned her Bachelor of Arts at the University of Tennessee while competing as a springboard and platform diver. She took the pre-medical track and incorporated anthropology, psychology, and Eastern religious studies. As a part of the College Scholars program, Jill wrote a thesis exploring addiction recovery and the interconnectedness of body, mind, and spirit in the healing process. During her time as a diver, she established an understanding and respect for the mind-body connection and the role that nutrition, sleep, and stress can play in overall health. Her personal health journey and a desire to practice a prevention and wellness-focused approach to healthcare led her to the Pacific Northwest to pursue a doctorate in naturopathic medicine and a master's in acupuncture at the National University of Natural Medicine. While in school, she focused her clinical rotations on adjunctive care for cancer and chronic disease, psycho-neuro-endocrino-immunology, and a Japanese approach to acupuncture. She spent extra hours learning Asian bodywork, craniosacral therapy, and myofascial therapy to integrate bodywork into her treatment style. Jill returned home to East Tennessee in 2018 to help develop the holistic health program at Blackberry Mountain. In her work, she strives to bridge different ways of knowing to promote wellness and support the individual path to health and healing. You can learn more about Jill and her approach to healing at https://ainsleyjillian.com

CHAPTER 5

EARTHING CHANGED MY LIFE

TAKE YOUR F*CKING SHOES OFF!

Olivia Smith

MY STORY

I stopped living the day my father died on Saturday in March of 2008. I often heard what a broken heart feels like but never experienced anything like the loss of my father. Still, that day, it felt like my heart ruptured and broke into a million pieces. I went into a state of paralysis. I was unable to interact with my closest friends and even my family. I felt invisible to myself and acted like a robot with no emotions.

At the time, I had a large spa and wellness center with over 50 employees and was responsible for creating new business and making payroll. I became physically and mentally exhausted. My oxygen level was running so low that my fingers and toes were a deep purple. My resting heart rate was chronically elevated above 100 beats per minute. Stressed and charged with anxiety, I felt hopeless and depressed and in pain.

During a visit with my doctor to get some sleep aids, he took one look at me and said that I must immediately stop and come to terms with my grief before the stress becomes life-threatening. So I decided to take a break and change my environment for a few days. There was a health and wellness conference in Hollywood, California, close to my home. I invited a few of my health-minded girlfriends to come along.

In the fall of 2013, we set up a small display table and filled it with brochures about our spa and wellness center to expense our trip. As we were bringing the table dressing and flyers in, I walked past an elderly gentleman on his knees, crawling around on the floor running wires under a group of chairs lined up along the wall. Attracting my attention, I stopped and watched for a few seconds and kindly asked, "what are you doing?" He looked at my purple feet, looked up at me, and said, "Please sit down and take your shoes off." He seemed a trusting soul, so I complied. He then took two simple electrode patches and placed them on the bottom of my feet. While asking for permission to ground my feet, he reached over and grabbed two cords he had placed under the chair and connected one to the patches on my feet. I thought to myself, this is weird, and asked, "What are you selling?" He replied, "I'm not selling anything; I just came to the show to ground people for the folks here who sell thermal imaging cameras. They send people over after they take an image, and I patch their feet and ground them to the earth for thirty minutes, just like I'm doing here with you. Then they go back and get a second image where they can see that the inflammation disappears." I asked if I could do the thermal imaging after setting up my table. He looked up and said, "You won't need to; sit here for a few minutes." He then went on about running his cords under the chairs. Not knowing what to expect, I just sat there and directed my friends as they came by to go on over and set up our table.

Suddenly, I felt a tingling in my feet and the pulsing of the blood in my legs. Then looking down at my toes, I was shocked to see that the color had gone from purple to my standard healthy skin color, and the pain in my feet and legs disappeared. Not having time to visit any longer, I asked if I could come back later. Then I asked if he had information on what this grounding was all about. He handed me a book called *Earthing*. I took the book and went to my table, puzzled that he did not have a booth or brochure at a trade show, and said he was not selling anything.

Throughout the day, I asked each of my girlfriends to go over and let him put the patches on their feet and come back and tell me what they felt. Everyone had a different story. One felt an emotional release in which she shared her entire life story with this stranger in less than 30 minutes. She came back a different person, being less stressed and much happier.

The next lady was timid and reluctant to have a man touch her, but she let him ground her feet with our persistence. Within minutes her demeanor changed, and she began to smile and carry on a lively conversation about life challenges. My third girlfriend had a similar experience; she said the feelings of the stress and tension in her body instantly drained away, and she began to feel good. She also began sharing personal challenges and family issues in her life with this perfect stranger.

That evening I took his book to the room and started reading, figuring out what this earthing was all about and what he was selling. I was sharing a hotel room with my girlfriends, and we talked half the night about the effects earthing had on them. Everyone wanted more, so the next day, we all signed up to get more earthing. And we began sending every one of our customers to do the same and asking them to come back and share their experience. As the day went on, we created a frenzy of activity around this gentleman who, on his knees, spent the whole day earthing and talking to everyone we sent over. Good for us that when people came back to share their stories, we were creating good relationships in selling the hell out of our products. It was fun and made working in the booth an exciting experience.

In all the activities, I recognized it was essential to learn as much as I could and find a way to bring earthing into my wellness center as I had never seen any product or treatment that so quickly and profoundly reduced stress and changed women's mental state.

The following day after returning home, I went outdoors barefoot to water the roses. Standing there, I felt the water slowly dripping on my feet and the dampened ground below when a sensation of energy began moving up my legs and into my body. My heart seemed to swell up, and I felt alive and vibrant. It seemed that my heart was opening like a rose. My stress and tension and hurried thoughts all seemed to drain away, and I felt fresh and full of happiness with a smile that I had lost some years before with the passing of my father.

How could just standing barefoot on the earth have such a profound effect on my body and mental being? I had to know more so I contacted the earthing man and asked if we could meet. He was most accommodating and came to meet at the wellness center. After some meet and greet, he suggested grounding clients with mats and grounded chairs while receiving treatments or services. I immediately agreed, and we earthed the entire center.

After weeks of seeing the women come in with stress imprinted on their faces and leaving with a sense of joy and peace and a smile on their faces, I shared these results with the earthing man, whose name is Clint. Confirming that he noticed the same results, he suggested I help produce a clinical study to validate these results.

A few weeks later, Clint introduced me to Gaetan Chevalier, who had already produced several studies measuring the biological effects of earthing. Together we created a study outline, presented it to an independent medical review board, and 30 days later, received permission to proceed. Upon completing the study and being peer-reviewed and published by the Journal of Cosmetics, Dermatological Sciences, and Applications in December 2014. (Grounding the Human Body Improves Facial Blood Flow Regulation)

With my growing understanding of earthing, I could only think about how this work needed to be shared with women everywhere. I wanted to sell my wellness center and work full time, speaking about earthing at wellness seminars and events across the country. As time went on, we were grounding up to 1500 people at the Longevity Conferences and hundreds at the Chopra center events, teacher conferences, and a host of other similar events.

After seeing and hearing so many women talk about their beneficial experiences from earthing, we decided the best way to share it with the most people would be to capture people's stories on film and produce videos. Over three years, the stories grew, and a film company turned them into an award-winning documentary, *The Earthing Movie, the Remarkable Science of Grounding*, has now been viewed by over four million people and growing monthly.

Now you know my story, and I'm just getting started!

THE TOOL

A tool is an item used with your hands to carry out a particular function. An example is a hammer, a tool used to hit a nail and drive it into the wood to hold boards together.

The tools I will refer to here are your feet. However, you will need a short lesson on adequately using these tools (your feet) to experience the life-changing wellness benefits mentioned earlier.

First, you need to know that the earth is a humungous battery forever charged by the sun. Further, all plants, animals, and people living in daily contact with the ground adsorb and become charged with this energy. And this really should be in Ripley's Believe it Not because what it does, you will never believe until you experience it. When charged with this energy, your body becomes electrified with a radiant glow as your heart rate and blood flow normalize. Even more critical, chronic aches, pains, and stress quickly melt away, leaving you with a feeling of aliveness and wellness. And the most exciting part to me is that I look many years younger in as little as fifteen minutes. That's because my facial skin circulation improves automatically. It's like getting the best facial ever for free and with no chemicals or appointments.

To receive these benefits and many, many more, all you need to do is take your f*cking shoes off and put your God-given bare feet back on the earth.

In 1960, the world's great minds invented the plastics that we now use for soles on the bottom of our shoes. Unknown was that plastic shoe soles cut off the earth energy that we now know prevents fatigue, chronic pain, and many inflammation-related health disorders.

Here are some recommendations on how to use your bare feet to restore your health and wellbeing. Go outdoors and sit on the ground and take your shoes and socks off. Note any pain, stiffness, fatigue, anger, or other feelings of stress you are experiencing. Then place the bottom of your feet flat on the earth. Within a few minutes, you will feel a slight tingling or energy moving up your legs. As it continues to move throughout your body, all muscle tension will begin to release, and your breathing will become easier. As the pain and fatigue begin to drain away, you will find yourself smiling and saying, why hasn't someone told us about this before. Some will say I've been in pain for thirty years. The pain is gone; I've got my life back! And just touching my feet to the earth makes it go away in minutes, like a miracle.

Once you get familiar with the feel of being charged up with Earth's energy and you, want more. There are many ways and places to reconnect your bare feet with the ground and get your life back. The best and easiest is to go outdoors, sit down, remove your shoes, and place your feet on the grass. If you do not have a yard or a nearby park with live grass, there are options. You can sit on your patio and put your feet on any unpainted concrete. Same for concrete sidewalks, they conduct earth's energy, so a barefoot walk around the block is ideal for draining stress and tension and reenergizing your body. A walk at the beach is maybe one of the best ways to recharge because you also get a good dose of sun-producing vitamin D, which is essential for health.

There are barefoot substitutes for those who don't have time to get their bare feet on the earth. These barefoot connection devices are readily available from the groundtherapy.com website and other products sites like Earthing.com.

For those who would like to learn more about the life-changing health benefits of connecting to the earth, earthinginstitute.net provides a host of published studies and articles from scientists worldwide.

When my bare feet are on the earth, I feel a force of warmth of a mothering spirit that runs through my being, calming and soothing my soul. I have tried here but cannot fully express the simple knowingness that I am one with all other people living in contact with the earth in harmony and health.

Please join me.

Take your f*cking shoes off and get your life back!

Olivia Smith is an Earthing Ambassador, Master NLP Practitioner, Master Hypnotherapy Practitioner, and co-founder of Tree Sisters. Olivia specializes in MER, the mental and emotional release technique, to release unresolved negative emotions and beliefs that hold us back from what we truly desire. Above all, Olivia is an advocate for women's empowerment. For years, she has put women and the importance of their mental and emotional wellbeing at the forefront of her mind, and it quickly became her driving force.

Olivia has had the honor and pleasure of working with women for many years. She realized her love of supporting and empowering women when she owned and operated her wellness center and spa for 17 years. And for the last seven years, in what she feels is her true calling; teaching women about the significant mental and physical health benefits of Earthing. The importance of leading women to health is her mission, as her passion for women's health and wellness has continued to blossom.

As an Ambassador for Earthing, Olivia worked with The Chopra Center in assisting attendees in experiencing the benefits of grounding. One of her proudest achievements as an Earthing Ambassador was co-producing "The Earthing Movie," which won many awards in the quest to bring the knowledge of grounding to the world. Olivia naturally gravitated towards the path of being a Master NLP Practitioner, another way to help women get to the version of themselves that they desire and that they deserve. Olivia lives to ground women physically and mentally to see their joy of positive transformation. Educating women about reconnecting their bodies with the earth is her purpose and her future.

In Olivia's free time, she enjoys her pilates class, barefoot walks, and hiking with her little Yorkie, Bodhi.

Let's connect:

Facebook: Olivia Smith (Ramirez)

Instagram: olivia_smith201

Email: oliviasmith394@gmail.com

CHAPTER 6

WHEN LIFE HANDS YOU LEMONS, TAKE THE HINT

MAKING THE SWITCH TO PLANT-BASED

Ann Keating

MY STORY

"You have cancer."

Not the words you ever want to hear from your doctor, but oddly, not the worst ones to come from her mouth. They were, however, the words that motivated me to take control of my health and destiny. This is not your typical cancer story.

It was March of 2013, and I had gone in for a routine mammogram the week before. I had no issues, no symptoms, nothing at all that would prepare me for the diagnosis. In fact, I always considered myself to be rather healthy; I rarely ate red meat, never smoked, wasn't much of a drinker (one glass of wine got me dizzy), loved my veggies, and exercised regularly.

But there it was, a diagnosis of breast cancer.

"It's very small and in an early stage," Dr. M added encouragingly. "If you have to have cancer, this is among the best scenarios."

Confident I had "the good kind of cancer," I quickly got recommendations for a surgeon, oncologist, and plastic surgeon. I refused to let this disease get the better of me, although my grandmother had succumbed to it. The treatment options were better, and my cancer had most likely been caught way earlier than hers. I was (am) most likely just plain more mule stubborn than she ever could have been. I was going to sail through all of this as though it was no more than a bad case of the flu.

"I want a double mastectomy," were the first words out of my mouth, "and reconstruction."

"Maybe you want to think about this for a bit," Dr. M suggested. "You don't need to make those kinds of decisions right away. Take a few days to think this over."

"Nope," I replied. "I want to be aggressive so that I never have to have this conversation again. And, besides, this is my opportunity to go from no chest to looking like Dolly Parton. They can stop expanding right before I tip over!" Our family has always survived worst-case scenarios by employing gallows humor. I don't know if it's because we are Irish or just really weird.

What followed was a round of doctor's visits, tests, and decisions.

The MRI was super easy. Lying facedown on the table with my face in the massage table "donut," I could almost forget why I was there. I didn't feel claustrophobic and wasn't in any pain at all. It didn't even last all that long. Easy breezy.

The biopsy, however, was another matter entirely.

"Lie on this table, and Nurse R will give you a back massage while the doctor gets the tissue sample," her accomplice promised me, much in the same way I imagine the witch lured Hansel and Gretel into sticking their heads into her oven.

An hour later, bruised and with enough holes poked in me that I was afraid to take even a sip of water for fear of leaking like a sieve, they called in a second doctor to try and get the samples. The promised back massage devolved into a series of pokes and prods that not only did *not* take my mind off the fact that the doctors seemed to think I was a human pincushion but was actually making things worse and more uncomfortable. I began to suspect that this medical team had graduated from the Marquis de Sade finishing school.

And still, that was not the worst.

"I will do the bilateral mastectomy, and Dr. Y will put in the expanders for the implants at the same time," Dr. M informed me when we met to discuss the results of all the tests and prepare me for the upcoming surgery. "But you won't be able to get the final implants until after you complete chemotherapy."

Chemo?! When did my "good cancer" go from easy breezy to chemo? Maybe she had the wrong patient. I was the one with early-stage cancer who had opted for the bilateral mastectomy, not the stage four patient who had no other choice.

"What?" I gasped. "When did chemo get put on the table?"

"Your oncologist will talk to you about options, but it turns out the markers of your cancer showed it to be more aggressive than we thought," she explained. "Your prognosis is still excellent, though."

Still not the worst words, but definitely in the top two or three.

The surgery went well, with the doctor convinced she got all of the cancer, although there was one worrisome spot where she couldn't tell definitively since the margin was so close to the skin, and I was still so bruised and swollen due to the biopsy from Hell. The expanders were in place, and I was quickly in recovery.

I know my family went through agony, but as the patient, all I remember is being wheeled into the operating room and telling the person pushing the bed that they were a very good driver, and they should try out for NASCAR. I told you that one drink made me dizzy, well one drip of anesthesia apparently had the same effect. The next thing I knew, I woke up to an annoying rendition of *All of Me* in a slurred, off-key alto. It took a moment or two, but I soon realized the contestant for the worst singer in the world was me!

The next day, I surprisingly didn't feel near as much pain as I thought I would. I really wasn't in any pain at all. The only thing that seemed to be wrong with me was a strange, sunburn-like rash on my arms and legs. The doctors chalked it up to a reaction from the wipes they had used pre-surgery and discharged me.

Two days later, my doctor was making a house call on Saturday and conferencing in my dermatologist. It turns out my rash was something called Stephen Johnson syndrome, and the next thing I knew, they were throwing around words like "steroids," "severe," and "hyperbaric chamber." This is not what you want to hear anytime, let alone after you've been diagnosed with cancer, told you are getting chemo, and then have a bilateral mastectomy. Actually, these are not words you ever want to hear. Way to kick a person when they are down.

Luckily, my doctors were able to get my latest situation under control, and so after about a week, I was back to just having to worry about dying from cancer and having chemo.

Not long after that, I once again sat in front of a doctor, my oncologist this time, and heard the dreaded word again: chemo.

"I recommend a twelve-week cycle of chemotherapy in tandem with a targeted therapy called Herceptin for a year." She handed me brochures explaining what chemo is, along with lists of potential side effects.

"Can I choose door number two?" I feebly requested.

"You are in good overall health," she reassured me, "so you should come through this without too much difficulty."

Famous last words.

One chemo treatment, a swollen face and neck, mysterious bruises, and what looked like another rash but turned out to be all of the blood vessels in both of my legs being broken simultaneously later, she told me that she was wrong.

"In order to even try to get you through the rest of your chemo, I would have to pump you full of so many drugs like steroids that you would not thank me," she explained. "We were only doing the chemo to be aggressive, so I think you will be fine without it. Hopefully, you won't lose your hair from just the one chemo treatment," she concluded as she sailed out the door. FYI, I did lose my hair.

Strangely, *these* were the worst words.

Why were they the worst? Because they meant that I had no hope of a medical cure. It meant I was on my own, fingers crossed, and hope for the best. Traditional medicine did all that it could for me, but it couldn't do everything. I didn't want the chemo, dreaded it, but it was at least something to hang on to.

I went home and immediately began to research alternatives to chemo. I practically drove my oncologist out of her mind with all of my "finds."

"There is a study in Texas. . ." I would begin.

"Nope."

"I heard they are doing experimental treatments with. . ." I tried again.

"Nope." She cut me off every time. "You are tolerating the Herceptin, and we are just going to keep a close eye on you. You are not one of the patients I lose sleep over at night."

Frustrated, I expanded my search.

And that's when I landed on the one thing I felt I could do that would give me the best chance for survival. That's when I stopped being a victim and became empowered. I would take back the control I lost over my body and my health. Food would become my medicine instead of taking some drug based on mustard gas. I would become vegan, which is kind of like becoming a super-hero with the power to transform food nobody really wants to eat into mouth-watering creations.

THE TOOL

It's a lot easier now to be vegan than it was in 2013. Restaurants are offering more options, and grocery stores are dedicating entire sections to plant-based foods, and most people no longer think of vegan as some strange, alternative lifestyle where you eat bark and howl at the full moon. Meatless Mondays are now a "thing."

All of that is great, but becoming vegan for health reasons can look quite different from being vegan for other reasons. There is a lot more to consider when you're trying to boost your immune system and avoid possible carcinogens than when you are simply trying to avoid meat every Monday.

How did I go about it? With some healthy tools.

BUY ORGANIC

The first thing I learned was to buy organic whenever possible.

There is a list called "The Dirty Dozen," which typically includes things like peppers, tomatoes, apples, and kale. These are fruits and vegetables where we consume the entire thing, skin and all. Therefore, we are consuming the pesticides that reside on that skin. The residue can linger even after washing and is a possible carcinogen, so I choose to hedge my bets and avoid non-organic whenever possible. I figure since I am consuming way more fruits and vegetables than most people, I want them to be as clean as possible.

Why don't I simply remove the skin of my non-organic apple? Because that is where so much of the fiber and so many of the nutrients are! Very often, we throw out different parts of food because it is undesirable or inedible. Tops of carrots? Trash. No, no, no! The tops of carrots are perfect for a lot of things like pesto (the leafy greens of farmers market carrots), or vegetable stock where you throw out the vegetables after all of the goodness and flavor has been cooked out of them. This is why I buy organic.

READ LABELS

The next thing I learned was how to become a detective.

I would stand for hours in grocery store aisles or online looking at the ingredients in pre-packaged food. Most of what I saw horrified me. I never realized how many chemicals or sugars and added salt were in foods with labels that had the words "nature," "healthy," or "good" in their titles. Yikes!

It turns out there is a difference between pure maple syrup and brands that have maple syrup as one of several ingredients. Nut butters can contain added sugars, oils, and salt that I do not need or want in my diet. Even buying something like dried fruit can get dicey if you opt for one that is sweetened with sugar as opposed to fruit juice.

Can I avoid things like sugar and salt altogether? No. Not if I don't want to be homicidal and have my family vote me off the island. What I can do, though, is limit them and try to keep the sources as pure and clean as possible. It's all about reducing the inflammation and boosting the immune system as much as possible, not about obsessing over every bite I put in my mouth and stressing myself out.

Once I found a few brands I could trust and products I liked, I no longer had to bring a sleeping bag and set up camp in aisle three of my local store.

Most of the switches are easy, and you won't even notice. Brown rice pasta made with only two ingredients (water and brown rice) tastes surprisingly similar to white pasta, especially when you cover it all with sauce anyway. Mix it half and half with spaghetti squash, and it's a win-win of added veggies and a healthier take on pasta.

Single-ingredient pumpkin puree is my choice over pumpkin pie puree. I can add my own spices and sweeten it more "naturally" on my own, eliminating things like cane sugar. Again, an easy swap that no one in my house knows I'm doing.

So now that I have researched my food and limited my grocery list to more healthy options, it's time to start cooking.

GET IN THE KITCHEN

While the internet abounds with vegan recipes and hacks and everything is labeled "The Best _____ Recipe Ever!" it can still be hard to make the final leap into healthier eating. Just because something is labeled as the best doesn't mean it is. I've tried lots of recipes over the years, and, trust me, they were not all winners. Sometimes I think tree bark would have tasted better.

What can you do? Find foods that are familiar to you and start there. Don't try to go hardcore all at once by trying foods that you are totally unfamiliar with.

If you are a fan of Mediterranean cuisine, start with hummus, but explore different flavors or how it can be used as a dressing for salads, a base for a seven-layer appetizer dip, or even an ingredient in a stuffed pepper or stuffed squash. It's not just for dipping raw veggies into.

Things like nachos and tacos are popular for a reason; they taste great! How about swapping out ground beef for pulsed, seasoned chickpeas and maybe plain lettuce for cabbage or kale? Play with spices and try the unexpected. Instead of corn chips, why not homemade (or frozen) sweet potato chips as a base for those nachos?

KEEP IT SIMPLE

Choose ingredients that do double duty.

Rolled oats can be a breakfast cereal or a muffin, cake, bread, crust, or binder in a veggie burger. You don't need a million flours, just a blender to transform the oats. Chia seeds or flax seeds can be used as toppings, to make pudding, as an egg replacement, or to thicken your smoothie.

Sweet potatoes are not just for dinner; they are also an appetizer, breakfast, or dessert. Plus, as an added bonus, the dog loves them as a snack! There are a lot of recipes I've created with common, easy-to-find ingredients and leftovers.

BUT WHERE DO I GET MY PROTEIN?

Protein is a huge worry for people when they explore a plant-based diet. It is probably one of the things they should worry about the least. Protein sources are many and varied.

A can of chickpeas can be roasted with spices and turned into a healthier, protein-filled snack or salad topping that is way better for you than a highly processed bag of something with a list of ingredients longer than your arm. They can also be the hidden ingredient in mouth-watering brownies.

Lentils, beans, and yes, I'm going to go there and say that four-letter word, tofu, can all be magically transformed into quick and easy meals. There are a wide variety of all of these, and if you haven't explored them, you might be surprised at how very different they all are and the endless ways they can be prepared.

I have found that by making some simple swaps, I'm able to create recipes reminiscent of food I grew up with, like pierogis or stuffed peppers. I have also branched out and created recipes based on some of my favorite restaurants or ethnic foods, so I don't get tired of the same three recipes every week. Vegan doesn't have to mean boring or a steady stream of salads and Buddha bowls (although they are yummy), and healthy doesn't have to be time-consuming and difficult.

Simple shifts have made a huge difference in my health and life.

Ann Keating is a vegan recipe developer and food blogger. She is a contributor for the online media publication Food Talk Daily and can be seen on Facebook live for Ekoe Health sharing her recipes, tips, and tricks.

As a former elementary teacher, she unites her love of teaching with her passion for creating new and exciting recipes for her clients. She works with everyone from novice cooks to more experienced home chefs, helping them make the switch to a more plant-based lifestyle.

She believes small changes can make big impacts, and her philosophy is that everyone makes these changes at their own pace and in their own time.

Ann guides clients through setting up their kitchens, shopping for healthy products, and even cooking along with them, tailoring her programs for both private and corporate clients alike.

Schedule a free 20-minute consultation to get started incorporating more plant-based dishes into your life by visiting her website.

Website: www.cantbeetplants.com

Instagram: @cantbeetplants

Facebook: CantBeetPlants

As a special gift for you, click on the following link for a special recipe.

www.cantbeetplants.com/sacredspaces

CHAPTER 7

LOVE YOUR HEART OUT

FINDING THE PATH TO YOUR GOLD

Angela Barbieri Usas

MY STORY

MY HEART

I cried myself through the first 41 years of my life. It's intense when you feel everything. My heart is like a soft-boiled egg. There's a soft, white layer around it, which is semi-protective, but if bounced too hard, the insides ooze out in the form of tears.

Bounce, bounce, bounce. Tears oozing. I could fill a whole ocean with the number of tears I've shed in this lifetime. My tears don't discriminate. They flow for all things, big and small. A sappy love movie? A person hurting? An episode of Who's The Boss? Check. Check. Check. These drops fall for painful experiences as well as joyous ones. Call me Queen Cryer.

I often felt alone because my tears were consuming. I got frustrated when I couldn't explain with words the truth I felt in my heart. I felt my way through life, but the world talks, so I got stuck. Coherent sentences evicted me when the grand rapids of emotion flowed. So I got quiet, felt shame, cried, and repeated.

Am I broken? I didn't know how to protect my heart, so it cracked a little more with each experience. If you looked at my heart under a microscope, you'd see cracks of all sizes. Long, short, deep, surface-layer, crisscrossed, and circular. Tears stream down my cheek right now as I write about my fragile heart.

When I don't know what to do, I go inward and pray. *Dear God, please be with me. I am hurting right now. Please hold me and help me through this pain.*

HIDING OUT

When I felt shame, I hid. I felt ashamed for not being enough. I hated not feeling smart enough or pretty enough. *What am I supposed to do with my life? Who am I? How the heck am I supposed to figure it out?*

It was easier when I was a child because I could break down crying on the regular. My big emotions were acceptable. But as I got older, I ran to the bathroom before tears erupted. I acted like the words said to me didn't feel like a punch in the stomach.

I cracked so many times in my adolescence. Crrrack. Crrrack. Crrrack.

I was deeply loved, but the bad stuff was easier to believe. I had negative thoughts run through my mind constantly, so the abundant love all around me had no chance of filling those Swiss cheese holes in my heart.

I got so tired of trying to express feelings with words, so I'd say, "I'm fine. I'm just tired. I'm fine, I'm fine. I'm just so tired."

When you don't know who you are or what you want to be, life is overwhelming. The world expects answers. How often do grownups ask kids, "What do you want to be when you grow up?" It's meant to be a conversation starter but, for me, it was a conversation stopper. "I don't know," was all I said. Then, the feeling of not knowing lingered.

To relieve the tightness in my chest and the lump in my throat, I journaled daily. I wrote my feelings out, copied song lyrics that moved me, and doodled. I buried my face into the blank pages, trying to shut the outer world out and figure out who I was and what my emotions were telling me. Those blank pages invited possibility, excitement, and wonder, but I filled most of them with anger, sadness, and splotched tear marks. Swiss cheese holes grew all over my heart. And more cracks, more scar wounds on an invisible organ inside me. I wondered if my heart would crack so much that it'd explode from excess sensitivity.

When I couldn't contain the collected emotions of my heart, I would sit on my dad's lap, even in my 20s, and let the river of tears flow. "Shh. Shh. Shhhh. It's okay, babydoll," he would say as he rubbed my back and took deep breaths. After the uncontrollable sobbing slowed down, the trembles and shakes lessened, I'd hear his slow, deep breaths more clearly and start to breathe in sync with him. Nice, slow, deep breaths. Another slow deep breath. And another. One more episode behind me—for now.

I prayed some more. *Dear God, why is life so hard? I try to be a good person, but I get hurt so easily. Why do people say such insensitive things? Please be with me and help me try to understand. I don't like crying all the time. I feel weak and dumb. I know you are here with me. Please stay with me. Guide me to what I'm supposed to do with my life.*

PEEKING IN

More life, more cracks. Definitely more tears. A whole boatload. I got used to the tears. I accepted them as part of me, which is great because they weren't leaving.

There is more within me than I realized. It was as if all those cracks in my heart created more space for the Divine to come in. I found myself drawn to different modalities, each one giving me another treasure, more golden nuggets for my collection. Who would've known cracking open was what I needed? My Swiss cheese holes were filling up with something better than before. In fact, without realizing it, my heart was practicing Kintsugi.

Kintsugi means "to patch with gold." In Japanese culture, cracked bowls are filled with gold to make them better than before. Life has hard lessons, but that's why we're here. We get to find the gold lining if we're willing.

My broken heart isn't broken after all. It was meant to crack, just like yours is. Within the pain, we find ourselves. When those cracks open up, the gold richness of our essence pours into the holes, and our brilliant ore shines. None of us are broken; we never were. We just need to remember we are loved beyond measure.

Dear God and Angels, thank you for guiding me to these treasures. Each step has cracked me open more, which has led me deeper into my sacred space. My heart isn't fragile. It's stronger than I ever knew. My egg-y heart transformed into a semi-precious stone. Please help me trust myself more. I know I am here to guide people to their heart space. I just don't know how yet.

SHOWING UP

In 2019, I got on a plane. The woman in my row was at the window seat crying. She was sniffling as quietly as she could, unable to contain her pain but trying hard to be invisible. I sat and closed my eyes. I felt my chest tighten, my heart ache, my throat form a lump, and a profound weight settled in.

It wasn't my pain—it was hers—so I took a few slow deep breaths and reached into my bag for crystals and Oracle cards. I never leave home without them. In fact, before I travel, I go to my crystal table to collect whatever stones I'm guided to. Then, I find the souls that need these stones on my travels.

I pulled an Oracle card to give me guidance on what to say, not knowing her circumstance. Then I prayed. *Dear God and Angels. Thank you for your presence and for being present with me. Please guide me on how to support this beautiful soul next to me who is suffering. Allow me to be a vessel to serve everyone's highest good. Thank you. And so it is.*

Then I wrote her a three-page letter with all the love from my heart. I told her I didn't know her, but I loved her. I told her everything was going to be okay. I could sense she was strong and could overcome whatever was causing her pain. I told her I was here for her. I was happy to talk or listen.

When I finished writing, I gently tapped her arm. I gave her a big, warm smile and handed her the pages and a Rose Quartz heart crystal. She looked confused. "This is for you," I said.

She sat and read the pages. I distracted myself until she turned to me and said, "I don't understand. I've never had anyone be so kind to me. I don't know what to say."

I smiled, "You don't have to say anything. I just want you to know you're not alone, and whatever you're dealing with, you will get through it. I feel a deep strength in you."

It felt like time stood still, and it was just the two of us for an hour. She had suffered a lot and doubted herself. She'd experienced challenging times. She had a rough relationship with her parents and with men. She had lost a baby and was terrified she wouldn't be able to conceive again, even though all she wanted was to be a mom.

"You will have another baby," I said. "I promise you. I can feel it. I'm certain you will be a mother. You'll be an incredible one too."

When we deplaned, we came back to our earthly reality. We kept looking for each other and waving through the airport as we made our way to and from the baggage claim.

Oh my gosh. I fully trusted myself. I tapped into the gold that had grown within my cracks. I let love guide me. I let the Divine work through me to guide another woman back home to her sacred space, home to her heart. If I choose to follow my sacred heart, I will radiate love, compassion, and acceptance of others because I have been fully loved and accepted. I now feel the Divine presence within me.

It's 2021, and I smile from ear to ear when I see her name pop up in my messages. The woman and I reconnected. And you know what? She has a four-month-old son. We talked for an hour and a half. It was as if no time had passed, except she now had a baby. I witnessed her with her son while we talked. I could feel the love she pours into him. She is an amazing mom, raising her son and giving him all he needs and more.

Our souls found each other in this lifetime for a reason. She gave me the chance to trust myself fully. I gave her the space to feel loved when she felt alone. I know her. I was her.

Others saw my big heart, love, and gifts before I did. I thought something was wrong with me, but my imperfections were what made me perfectly me.

Dear Mother/Father God and Angels. Thank you for cracking me open to be a vessel for love. I am honored, humbled, and grateful. Thank you for guiding me to help this woman feel loved. I feel strong and empowered. Now, my semi-precious stone heart is radiating light out to others. I know what I am here to do. Thank you for being with me and transforming my emotional heart into golden love.

NOW

After decades of crying and doubting, I'm in awe of how amiss my perception of myself was. I had no reason to hide or feel shame. I came into the world as a bright light. An emotional light, but big and bright.

I wasn't broken. I wasn't alone. I was willing. I was open. I was strong enough to be split wide open, so the Divine could shine love through me.

My heart is my superpower.

I know who I am: *I am love. I am whole. I am complete. I have all the answers to everything I need in my big, beautiful heart. We are all capable of feeling this abundant, radiant love. It is within each and every single heart. We just need to be willing to crack wide open and fill up with gold.*

I am exactly who I'm supposed to be and where I'm supposed to be right now. At 42, I am here to share my heart with the world and guide others to open theirs. I still cry, but not as often and rarely about sad things. Now, my cheeks dampen because I am so moved and touched by how overwhelming love is. I wish I could give others my heart to hold to see how beautiful it is to be kind to yourself, honor yourself, and trust that you have everything you need within you. If you put my heart under a microscope now, you'd need sunglasses because the beaming gold is so bright.

Will you join me in remembering who you are? Tune into your heart, and I promise you'll find your whole self there. It's not an easy path, but it's worth every single tear. I promise. We are all Divine beings. I love you, I really do.

Dear Mother/Father God and Angels, thank you for the beautiful souls here who witness my story. Please guide them to remember they are whole, perfect, and complete, just as they are. Please help all those who think they are cracked and broken to realize those aches fill up with gold and love. We are never alone. I love you.

THE TOOL

Some say tools and toolboxes, but I love treasures and treasure chests. Do you feel me? I have a treasure chest full of treasures, and I'm still collecting. You never know which treasure you'll need to sparkle at any given moment.

The beauty of the treasure I'm sharing with you is you already have it. It may be dusty, underused, and dim, but we can polish it right up and get it shining bright. You've had this treasure all along. Your heart is the grandest, most radiant, and precious treasure of all. Your heart is so big and so powerful that it can transform anything negative into everything positive.

We can choose to live with fear or with love. There's no mucky middle. Every action and reaction is based on one of these two emotions. Our ego resides in our head, and our soul resides in our heart. Ego has fear, focuses on outcomes and what we aren't. Soul only has love, knows everything happens in Divine timing, and you are enough.

When we live in our headspace, we bounce ferociously like a ping pong ball all over our brain with thoughts like, *Ugh, why didn't I do laundry yesterday? Why didn't I work out today, especially since I ate that cookie? I can't believe I said that to Sophia. I'm so tired. Why did I do that? What was I thinking? That was a terrible decision; I can't believe I did that! Oh crap, I forgot to send that email. What an idiot.*

However, when we drop into our hearts, it's a gorgeous garden of warm fuzzies, Care Bear love, beauty, and grace. *Oh, those yellow leaves are so gorgeous! Hi love, you look radiant today. I am so grateful I can walk and take in this beauty. Gosh, I love her. I am so proud of myself for doing that. She lights up the world. That nap was just what my body needed. I love how I showed up today. Life is amazing!*

My treasure is a heart-opener pose. By opening your heart, you'll tap into the divine and golden wisdom that is your birthright. This audio version is my personal favorite because you can close your eyes and go deeper into your heart. Click here: https://bossladybio.com/radiantheart/

Otherwise, here are the steps to follow:

Drop into your heart: Put your left hand on your heart, then your right hand over your left. Take a slow inhale and then exhale as if you're blowing through a straw. Take another inhale and this time exhale out of your mouth, making an audible "ahhh." Do that a few times to quiet the mind and settle into your heart. When there's no chatter in your head, take a minute or two to focus on your breath.

Set an intention and pray: Acknowledge yourself for being here. What do you intend? Do you want to open your heart to love? Do you want to let go of stress and anxiety? Do you want more self-acceptance? State an intention and/or pray. Use whatever word most resonates with you for a higher power. For example: "Dear God, I am grateful for your presence.

Please help me release the stress in my life and open my heart to serve my highest good."

Settle into position: I like to use a foam roller (positioned vertically along the spine) or a towel (placed horizontally across the bra line) to open my chest and heart. I like my arms in cactus position, but you can put your arms wherever feels best. Recenter for a minute by focusing on your inhale and exhale coming from your heart center.

Imagine a light: Imagine a small white or gold circle at your heart center that's the size of a seed or grape. With every inhale, let the shape of the circle grow, and with every exhale, shine the light brighter. Choose circle sizes that resonate with you—for example, seed-grape-kiwi-orange-pumpkin-watermelon. Keep the circle growing until it's all around you, like a big, protective bubble. Stay here for a few minutes, taking it all in.

Feel your heart: In this grand, love-filled light, how do you feel? Are you smiling? Do you feel joy? Does your body feel light? Do you feel how immense your love is? Stay present in the body, releasing thoughts and soaking in love. Love, love, love.

Give gratitude: Your heart is sacred. It's the home to your soul, where all your radiance and abundance live. Be grateful for your big, beautiful heart and all the love you have within. You are whole. You are complete. You are perfect just the way you are.

Closing: Bring your hands to your heart. Intend to hold onto this loving feeling throughout your day. If you find yourself in your head again, place a hand on your heart, take a few breaths (exhale through the mouth with a few "ahhs" to quiet the mind) and think of your white or gold bubble. This helps to keep your heart open.

Angela Barbieri Usas is best known for her tears and her loving heart. Ask her husband and three kids, and they'll vouch for her waterworks. Since Angela feels all the feels, she meets you where your heart is and guides you to remember you are whole and loved.

She's got a handful of certifications that she combines in her offerings as a Heart Guide. Her certifications include 200-hour Yoga TT, Prenatal Yoga, Health Coach, Reiki Practitioner, and Postpartum Doula.

Angela is a joyful crystal collector. She creates intuitive jewelry out of crystals, making one-of-a-kind bracelets, necklaces, and malas. Angela also has quite a collection of oracle cards and will gladly pull a FREE card for you in gratitude for being here. Just click on https://www.radiantheartcenterva.com/connect to connect with her and find more treasures while you're at it.

Instead of keeping up with her FB and IG pages, Angela loves live connection. Go old school and call or text her at: 571-215-1773. You can also contact her through www.radiantheartcenterva.com

If you can't refrain:

IG: @radiantheartcenterva

When not trying to cram her whole life story into a chapter, you can find her at home sipping her chai delight, driving to and from sports practices and games, playing fetch with her pup, or taking a nap while the kids and hubs are out. Shhhh, it's our little secret.

CHAPTER 8

SHADOW WORK

FINDING LIGHT IN THE DARKNESS OF TRAUMA

Christina Kauffmann

The lotus flower blooms from thick mud in murky waters. The flower makes its way up until it breaks the surface and emerges beautifully to greet the sun. When it's time for the sun to rest, the lotus does the same. It finds its way back into the mud, then repeats the cycle of resurrection and blooms just as beautiful as before. In life, adversity is the mud, the world is the murky water, and you are the lotus flower. The process to reach the top is just as important as what waits on the other side. The lotus flower does not hold all its beauty in its petals but rather in its journey from dark to light.

MY STORY

I'm wearing my favorite SpongeBob pajamas as I stand in the center of my bedroom, frozen. My heart beats fast, my body numb from the elevated pulse. My breath is shallow as I gulp for air through a stream of tears. Squeezing my eyes shut, panic sets in.

What is happening? Why is he hurting her? She's so much smaller than him! God, please let her be okay.

Time is standing still. My dad bursts through the bedroom door, jaw clenched, arms flexed, and walks towards me. *The room is spinning.* I've never seen this look in his eyes before. *Does he know it's me, his little girl?*

My chest tightens. His six-foot, 250-pound stature towers over my tiny five-year-old existence. "What happens at home stays at home!" he growls. He's out the bedroom door just as quickly as he charged into it. *Bam!* The walls to our home rumble like thunder as the front door slams behind him.

The bang of the door shakes me into the realization that I'm not dreaming; this nightmare is really happening. I suddenly realize my mom is kneeling in front of me. *When did she come in? Am I still standing? Have I said anything to her?*

I notice her disheveled pajamas and hair. Staring into her dark brown eyes, I again see something I've never seen before: horror. "It's okay, baby; he didn't hurt me. It's okay." She repeats calmly.

I still haven't moved. We're both in the center of my bedroom, but the room now feels twice the size. *Did I shrink? I feel so small.* My mom holds me, and I melt into the newfound darkness of my reality.

Okay, I've just shared something with you I kept to myself for 20 years. It's my earliest memory in the collection of "scary times" from the first decade of my life. The first of many moments that may have lasted only a few minutes in time but stayed with me forever.

For most of my life, I carried a deeply rooted sense of helplessness. The weight gradually grew heavier at every stage of my development from childhood to adulthood and peaked in my teen years. A significant life change along with the pressure to meet social and societal standards would destroy any bit of self-worth I had left. I didn't thrive in my stages of self-development; I simply survived.

"So why did you move all the way here?" I was asked for the hundredth time halfway through the first day of sixth grade. "For family." I'd answer, wishing it was that simple. *We're safe here.* Looking up to the sky, I'd pray that thought was true. By the age of ten, adapting was my superpower. My parents divorced when I was a toddler, and my mom had full custody of me. As an only child, it was her and me against the world from the start. We moved apartments at least once a year when we lived in Tucson, so I thought I'd easily handle moving to Pittsburgh, where I'd visited multiple times. In hindsight, the excitement I felt around the move was actually relief.

My dad wore an orange jumpsuit for a lot of my life. He was in and out of jail or prison and dealt with a lot of his own demons with addiction. When my dad was "doing good," I saw the side of him I wished would stay. His tall, muscular build made a statement when he walked into a room, and he knew just how to bully his way to what he wanted. He intimidated others without trying, but as his daughter, I had no reason to be scared of him until he showed me otherwise.

To this day, I can't imagine anything worse than seeing someone you love in pain and not being able to do a damn thing about it. The times my dad put his hands on my mom in front of me are still the worst days of my life. The physical abuse was not often, but the torment it created was never-ending. I was never the direct victim of his wrath, but as he hurt the most important person in my world, I was tortured by the inability to help her.

My survival instincts worked overtime, the playful side of my personality shut down, and I became "the quiet one" in a crowd of people. After the big move across the country, we were physically safe from the problems involving my dad, but my "new" life quickly presented its own challenges. Desperate to fit in, I downplayed what I'd gone through and deeply buried the hurt I didn't have time for. I'd continue this narrative through high school and college, eventually bringing it into the life I was starting to create as an adult.

Over the years, my repressed emotions manifested into numerous un-diagnosable physical health problems, clinical depression, and crippling anxiety. As my physical and mental health greatly declined, I knew if I didn't start to reclaim power over my life, the darkness would swallow me whole.

"The voice I finally heard that day was my own—the girl I'd locked away at ten years old, the girl I was before the world told me who to be—and she said: Here I am. I'm taking over now."

–Glennon Doyle

"We're going to try a visual meditation today if you're comfortable with that," says my mentor, Amy. We've been working together in private sessions to explore the mental roadblock that's had me stuck throughout my yoga teacher training and mentorship. Hesitating, "Okay, sure," I answer.

Adjusting my posture, I crisscross my legs and slide a yoga block under my sit bones to prepare. Closing my eyes, the pressure in my chest slightly lightens. *Let's give it a go.*

"First, remember you're safe here, and we can stop this practice at any time," Amy assures me. I nod my head in agreement and settle in with a few deep breaths. In a gentle tone, she begins to guide me. "Okay, start by bringing to mind a time when you were younger that felt stressful or upsetting. Stick with the one that first comes up and imagine you are witnessing this memory of little Christina, not experiencing it."

My stomach drops. My mind quickly picks that first memory I wrote about at the beginning of this story. A five-year-old me, frozen in the middle of my bedroom. *After 20 years, why the hell is this the first one coming to mind?! Jeez, little Christina looks terrified.*

Amy continues, "Now imagine your present-day self walks through the door to greet little Christina right where she is. You grab her hand and walk with her through a different door that opens to anywhere in the world you love to go." *The beach.* "Take a seat next to each other and do your best to comfort her through what she's feeling." Tears begin to roll down my face, and the ache in my belly has reached my throat. Fully immersed in the visual, I try to find the words to comfort this younger version of myself as we sit in the sand together. *You're safe now. You don't need to be scared anymore; I've got you. It's okay to cry. You're not alone. Everything is going to be okay.*

My tears turn to a soft cry, and though my eyes are still closed, I feel Amy's support surrounding me. "Gently grab little Christina's hand again and start to take a walk in this loving place you've come to. Now again, become the witness and observe from a distance your present-day self and younger self walking hand in hand until they're no longer in view. When you are ready, slowly begin to bring awareness back to your breath." *How do I feel good right now?*

Genuinely surprised by the strong emotions that resurfaced and the self-compassion I felt that day, I became determined to understand how to unbury the burdens in my heart. I began to explore how the mind, body, and soul hold on to experiences of emotional distress physically, energetically, and unconsciously over time. My emotional freedom grew by connecting the pain I was feeling in the present to the part of me that went through it. I had no idea I was embarking on the greatest journey of my life when I committed to diving deep into the dark parts of my story.

The time I've dedicated to learning about the physiological impact of trauma has been life-changing and incredibly empowering. Ignorance is not bliss! I've grown closer to both my parents since I've found the strength to speak up for little Christina and share my side of the story with them. At the same time, I've received a lot of answers I didn't know I needed. Learning more about my parents' lives during my childhood has helped me explore a different narrative. I'm not at all justifying my dad's behavior or every decision my mom made, but I am choosing how I remember my own experiences.

For too long, I felt like a victim in a world out to get me, but it was really something within me of which I was most afraid. Despite everything, my life has never had a shortage of love, and now, I consider loving my superpower. I've transformed constant feelings of frustration, fear, and despair into compassion, forgiveness, and contentment. I am sincerely grateful for every family member, friend, acquaintance, and experience that has brought pleasure and pain into my life. I know with the right tools and support system, the same can be true for you.

THE TOOL

Repressed emotions manifest as the "shadow" because the pain is unprocessed. The pain rules the subconscious and provokes hidden wounds until you move from avoidance to understanding. Shadow work is the path of exploring unprocessed pain, grief, and emotion. The "shadow self" was coined by psychologist Carl Jung, but the concept of understanding the layers of our being is nothing new.

Shadow work can look like:

- Accepting that you grow most outside your comfort zone.
- Learning to be patient with your progress.
- Focusing on your breath when your body is under stress.
- Questioning your thoughts and trusting your intuition.

- Choosing not to expend energy in over-explaining your feelings.
- Giving yourself permission to rest.
- Revisiting your 'why' over time.
- Shining your light for the world to see.

Most of us know someone who's gone through something we could never imagine. However, a hierarchy of hurtful experiences does not exist. Trauma is not measured by what happened but rather by the imprint it left inside you. If something upsets you, there is nothing too small for the possibility of an underlying impact. *Every emotion you feel is personal to your experience and is valid without an explanation.* Let me say that again. Every emotion you feel is personal to your experience and is valid without an explanation. The choice to explore what has hurt you—and why—is a decision only you can make for yourself.

Finding light in the darkness of trauma is a practice that looks different every day. Some of your greatest lessons will come from looking at the parts of yourself you hide away. I invite you to use the acronym below as a practice of learning how to deal with strong emotions. You can use LIGHT as a journal prompt or as in-moment practice when a strong emotion arises.

L - Listen. Imagine your emotion is a loved one that's upset and needs your support. Instead of immediately responding, take a moment to fully hear what they're telling you.

I - Identify. How do you feel as you listen to what your emotion is saying? Are you sad? Afraid? Angry? Frustrated? Or is it a combination? Just notice and recognize what comes up.

G - Greet. Acknowledge and show your understanding. You've listened, sat through the discomfort, and now you can choose how to best respond to your emotion instead of reacting to it.

H - Hold. Pause in this moment of accomplishment. You've supported your emotion in the way it needed because you listened to it first. Take some big breaths, stretch, walk, and give yourself a little tender care.

T – Transform. Continue to build a positive narrative around how you'll handle similar situations in the future. Your relationships look different with every emotion, but each one will grow stronger every time you face tough times together.

The key is to observe your shadow, not identify with it. It's possible to be aware of your thoughts and emotions without getting lost in the stories created around them. You are the consciousness behind the mind, and when you separate yourself from the clutter, what has held you down will begin to be what lifts you. You can't change the past or control the future, but you can write your narrative in the present. As you do the work of caring for your whole self, remember to meet yourself where you are. There will be different phases of your awakening, and wherever you are as you read this is exactly where you need to be. It's a marathon, not a sprint. You can be happy, healing, and hurting at the same time.

You have within you all that's needed, but I highly encourage finding professional and personal support to bring along on this journey with you. My own shadow work has been supported by therapy, yoga, and the loving people who've held space for me. The tool I shared with you is simply a place to start or revisit near the surface level of your transformation.

An itch for change is the trigger to search for answers. Introspection and realization lead to the discovery of your power and potential. Shadow work illuminates the path for transforming pain into freedom. Internally, I define a sacred space as a feeling of safety, peace, and wholeness. A feeling found not by fixing or finding yourself but by coming home to who you are.

Christina Kauffmann has a vision of a world in which people embody the root of their true self: love. Her life changed when she found yoga or as she believes, yoga found her! Beyond the physical practice, she's discovered the tools to cultivate introspection, self-awareness, and mindfulness. She holds a Bachelor's degree from West Virginia University (Let's Go Mountaineers!) and continues to expand her knowledge in the wellness space. Christina is a certified yoga teacher and has completed an extensive amount of trauma-informed yoga training to better share the practice in a safe and accessible way. Along with yoga, Christina is passionate about the use of cannabis as a natural alternative to support mental health and physical well-being. As a certified CBD advisor, she strives to educate others on the non-intoxicating, therapeutic benefits of the plant. Christina has lived in six different states, studied abroad in Hungary, and has traveled to almost 20 countries. She *loves* to talk about travel, meet new people and deeply connect with the world around her (a Scorpio, if you couldn't tell). Her mission, both personally and professionally, is not just to help others heal but rather to empower others to heal themselves. Visit https://onamission.bio/christinak to work with her, collaborate, or become a new close friend!

CHAPTER 9

COME HOME TO YOUR TRUE NATURE

TAKE A WALK TO LOSE YOUR MIND AND FIND YOUR SOUL

Tansy Jane Dowman

MY STORY

It was the day of winter solstice 2020 that my epic lightbulb moment arrived. Or perhaps more appropriately, you could call it a *Holy Shit!* moment. You see, a whisper grew inside of me that was repeatedly shoved down into the depths of my denial. A place of secrecy even I wasn't willing to listen to until that whisper became a roar.

I was out for a gentle, reflective walk that morning to honor the solstice and, returning home, felt the unusual urge to have a bath. The irony of this scene, which will make sense as you read on, is that I actually don't enjoy baths. They make me restless, and I always make them too hot. I fidget, overheat, and get annoyed at myself. Within minutes, I'm admitting defeat and climbing out wondering *what is wrong with me because a good soak in the bath is what all women love*, so I thought.

On this day, however, I felt a sense of ritual, so I heeded the call. I put on a podcast to help with the expected restlessness. I knew it was a good tool for keeping me in the bath longer than five minutes, and I was also in a phase of deep and intensive research to explore that voice inside. One that was still under the mercy of my ego and had definitely not been granted permission to speak out loud.

As I lay there listening carefully to Dr. Sari Solden, she said something that felt like she could have been sitting in my bathroom, talking directly to me. Her words carried through the haze of steam delivered directly to my soul.

"Many women with undiagnosed ADHD are suffering in silence, terrified that they are getting Alzheimer's."

My breath shot up into my chest and froze, trapped like a ball of cement with no escape.

Holy shit, fuck.

Dr. Solden named my deepest, most secret fear. I already checked the box on an overwhelming amount of ADHD traits and symptoms, but my mind continued to tell me I was mistaken, desperate to hold onto a different persona, frightened of the alternative.

This was different, though. What she said was a fear I was carrying around for years but did everything to suppress and ignore. A dark and frightening thought I didn't share with anyone because I knew people wouldn't take me seriously, and I was afraid to be vulnerable with that fear. Frightened they would think I was overreacting or ignore my fear completely and chime in with, *oh God, me too!* I even thought on a rational level I was overreacting, but deep down, I knew something wasn't right as I battled with intense and alarming memory blanks and relentless short-term memory challenges, to the point that it frightened me.

Dr. Solden continued speaking, but I didn't hear her words. Slipping into a daydream state, I replayed those frightening memories while her sentence played over in my mind. It was the un-mitigating evidence my ego needed to finally surrender and accept that the voice fighting to be heard was speaking my truth.

I have ADHD. Oh fuck I have ADHD! How the hell did I not know this before? I have ADHD! Oh my God, I just know I have ADHD.

I collapsed under the surface of the water as reality hit me. A gut-wrenching sob escaped from my mouth as the truth shuddered through my bones. Tears streamed down my face into the water. I was lying in a pool of grief and shock, mixed with relief and clarity, yet tinged with terrifying uncertainty.

What the hell is happening, and what the fuck am I going to do now!? How am I going to tell Dan? What will Mum and Dad say? What will my friends think? No one will believe me. Oh God, I need help. I have ADHD.

Six weeks later, I sat opposite a psychiatrist and received an official ADHD diagnosis, which gave powerful permission for something existing silently within for 43 years, to finally be acknowledged. A deeply embedded mask fell away, but its hold over me and the beliefs it created still battled in my mind. Even though I unveiled this aspect of myself, I continued to hold a deep fear of what others would think. I worried how people would see me and was terrified I would be rejected. I felt embarrassed and sad that I managed to bury this part of myself for so long. Imposter syndrome raged.

I'm supposed to be a wellbeing practitioner and life coach promoting connection to nature and the self, and I've been disconnected from this part of me all my life! Oh God, I feel like such a fraud. What will my clients think of me? How do I explain this? Shit shit shit.

Like so many people, I desperately wanted to fit in and remain in the right boxes. I didn't want to be different; I didn't want to admit I'd been hiding parts of myself or that I needed help, and I definitely didn't want to be seen as a burden or make a fuss. I wanted to be seen as the strong, independent, reliable, grounded, calming woman I presented for so many years. An image and persona that felt safe, accepted, and agreeable.

As I write this, my inner voice is offering me another lightbulb moment.

Did you think you were neuro-typical when you decided to hug trees for a living? Do you think perhaps your neuro-diversity is the exact reason and gift for you finding your life's purpose and passion and is the source of your capacity for deep empathy, creativity, and expression?

FITTING IN IS NOT BELONGING.

Isn't it crazy how humans have come to fear and judge difference or diversity, yet we see it displayed and celebrated unashamedly in the rest of nature? As Gary Ferguson put so powerfully,

"This beautifully rich and robust planet is, in all seasons, nothing if not a constantly unfolding testament to the essential power of diversity."

Agonizingly, humans have forgotten a deeply scientific and spiritual fact that has changed my life.

WE. ARE. NATURE.

We're not separate from the rest of nature, but like wayward teenagers, we've drifted from the path of being, lost our identity, and taken considerable risks to prove we are enough. Our pursuit for unobtainable success has turned us away from the wisdom and life force energy that not only created us but paved the way for us to come into existence. Our being here, as a result of 4.6 billion years of evolution, is a pure miracle and one that makes us more 'enough' than we will ever truly come to understand.

Being in nature with the unwavering belief that 'I am nature' has opened my eyes to an overflowing display of truth and guidance. When I observe the behaviors and principles of nature, I can shed the layers of limiting and false beliefs that the human world has created. All the expectation, stereotyping, judgment, shame, and fear that forces us to mask holds no value in nature where diversity is applauded, and acceptance is embodied in every second of its unfolding.

Nature doesn't hurry, and nature doesn't compare. Trees grow side by side following completely different journeys of growth, shape, and style, and I guarantee it's the one that's growing in odd, misshapen ways that will get more attention. When you acknowledge you are nature, you realize you belong to something so much bigger than the human world alone. You remember you're unique and don't need to fit into anyone's box or seal of approval. Your individuality is your strength and beauty. Diversity *strengthens* us as a community, just like biodiversity strengthens the entire ecosystem that keeps us alive.

NATURE IS MY MEDICINE.

It gives me goosebumps to think of how I intuitively cultivated an intentional relationship with nature seven years ago. It wasn't something I planned, and I remember it felt like something was calling out to me from those fields I would walk in every day. I couldn't fully understand it back then, but it was like someone calling me home or nudging me to remember something I'd forgotten. What I felt in those fields had a powerful impact and formed an unbreakable bond.

When nature called me home, I trusted in that pull and followed the instinctive trail of breadcrumbs my soul wanted me to go after. I found myself naturally slowing down and going against the ingrained need to walk fast. Instead of putting nature into the background noise of my mind, I gave it center stage and offered my heart-centered attention. I played listening games and noticed my busy mind ceased when I listened deeply to the song from the birds and accompaniment of the wind. I allowed myself to pause, sit on benches, and simply to be—such a bold act in these days of relentless productivity. I let my eyes roam freely and allow my gaze to fall upon detail and motion and the vast outline of the landscape pressing into the sky.

Little did I know back then how deeply important that connection with nature would be for me. Now the mask is off, I can be honest about who I truly am, and I want you to know that I *need* nature in my life. I don't mean I need to live in the countryside and go on weekend strolls and dog walks. I need to have an intentional and meaningful relationship with nature because it offers me such deep support for emotional health and wellbeing and gifts me with a powerful sense of identity and belonging. Nature is one of the only places I feel truly grounded and calm, and that is the vital medicine and support I need for my ADHD. It just so happens that I'm also fascinated by nature to the point I've carved out a career guiding others to create their own unique connection.

Perhaps there is a connection waiting out there for you too. It might be a sanctuary for peace to escape the chaos. It might be a silent voice within you that fears judgment from the human world and wants to feel held and accepted by Mother Nature as she meets you exactly as you are. Or there may be a restlessness that lives within you too and longs to feel grounded and rooted into being. Whatever that whisper or longing is, perhaps nature can guide you home to the truth of your own unique and beautiful nature.

THE TOOL

TAKE A WALK TO LOSE YOUR MIND AND FIND YOUR SOUL

AN INVITATION

This script has been written to guide you on a walk of connection with nature in a location and time of your choice. It could be in a park, a forest, or even your garden, as long as you are surrounded by an array of nature. You can read this as you walk, or you can download the audio version from the link below and let my voice be your guide. I invite you to allow at least 20 minutes for this practice but if you feel you want to extend the time, go ahead. Remember, your journey is unique to you so go with your own intuitive flow.

This is an invitation to take yourself on a walk of presence and connection and move beyond the mind and its need for logical answers. Creating time and space for this practice is an act of self-love, so give the task-focused mind permission to pause. You are a human being, not a human-doing, so see if you can let go of answers and outcomes and place your trust in the unfolding.

AN UNSPOKEN CONVERSATION

Walking attentively in a wild space is like having an unspoken conversation with Mother Nature. A conversation that needs no words but is an exchange of presence, instinct, sensations, and love. In this conversation, you let the body lead the way and allow your physical being time to connect with Mother Nature, inviting her in through all your senses. The pathway of experience begins with the senses. They are the avenues with which we learn, perceive, and become aware. They are the tentacles that connect us to the generous present moment, plugging you into the here and now. The more attention you can give to them, the more potent your experience will be.

CROSSING THE THRESHOLD

Before you begin walking, it's powerful to acknowledge your arrival and feel a sense of connection for the space you're about to enter into. Take a gentle look around and imagine you are standing at a threshold, ready to leave the human-made world for a while and cross over to a place created by the same life force energy that created you. Recognize that the nature you're going to walk with is living, breathing, and communicating in its own unique way. Take a moment to breathe and allow the tranquillity of nature to beckon you in with its invitation of generosity.

GET OUT OF YOUR HEAD AND INTO YOUR BODY

Resist the need to walk fast and get somewhere and begin walking slowly with awareness. Notice your feet pressing down on the earth with every gentle intentional step. Observe how instinctively your body knows how to move through the complex motion of walking. Your body is your animal self, wildly present with sensory awareness. It's the birthplace of your instinct, compassion, and courage and is where your aliveness begins.

Your mind will undoubtedly want to tag along, and it's all too easy to go on a walk trapped in your headspace. Reassuringly offer your mind a back seat so that other aspects of your being have space to take the lead. Let your senses out to play in this sensory playground and ignite a child-like sense of curiosity for all the things around you that get taken for granted through the lens of adult life.

YOUR EYES ARE THE WINDOWS OF YOUR SOUL

Gaze gently around you as you walk, filling your sense of sight with the abundance of diverse plant species around you. The trees and plants you offer your attention to are located in the present moment, so allow your eyes to connect with the here and now by consciously acknowledging what you see instead of letting it fade into the background. Imagine you are at an art gallery or sacred shrine, mesmerized as you take in every detail of color, shape, pattern, and texture.

ARE YOU REALLY LISTENING?

We hear things every day, but do not always truly listen, so bring your attention to your ears and sense their shape and formation. Imagine your ear canal is a direct route to your heart center and allow the sounds around you to flood in and fill your soul. The frequency of birdsong is at the sweet spot of the human ear and offers relief to weary, nervous systems. Listen as if the birds are performing just for you.

TOUCH IS THE FIRST LANGUAGE WE SPEAK

Let your hands continue this unspoken conversation and explore your sense of touch with the plants and trees around you. Take moments to pause and close your eyes, allowing you to tune even deeper into your sensory awareness. Notice how the different textures make you feel or what they remind you of. Trace the outline of objects and notice even the most subtle textures like the veins in a leaf or the velvet-smoothness of a petal.

THE SWEET SMELL OF PEACE

With your hands fresh from their connection to nature, hold them up to your face and breathe in their scent—earthy, woody, floral, or pine aromas that may be subtle but detectable with heightened senses. Breathe deeply and imagine the goodness of this smell, nourishing your body like an organic essential oil.

BE MORE TREE

If you are in a place with trees, go to one that catches your attention. If not, choose any plant, bush, or flower. Offer your undivided attention and explore it with your senses, noticing every detail. Consider the journey this species has been on from seed to current growth. What season is it moving through? How old could it be? If this tree could talk, what wisdom would it offer? What does it want you to know?

Stand facing it for a moment, bringing awareness to your feet connected to the earth. Close your eyes and visualize small shoots appearing on the soles of your feet that push down into the earth like the roots of a tree. Let those roots grow bigger and stronger, pushing deeper into the earth, and imagine them connecting with the tree or plant in front of you. Breathe down into feet, feeling grounded and rooted into this moment and able to receive the energy of protection and nourishment that Mother Earth provides in abundance.

THE GIFT OF RECIPROCITY

As your walk reaches its end, take a moment to reflect on your journey and the sensory experience you have received. Consider any insights or wisdom that you can bring into your life that will support you to become more nature. Turn around and offer an unspoken energy of gratitude and reverence for this sacred time of shared connection.

The name **Tansy** comes from the tenacious wildflower that grows in the English countryside, and much like her wildflower counterpart, Tansy lives and thrives in the countryside of Kent in the UK with her husband, two children, and side-kick dog. Nature is a fundamental part of her life, in work, rest and play.

Tansy is a Certified Forest Bathing & Natural Mindfulness Guide and ICF Personal Evolution Coach, utilizing nature as a tool for inspirational growth and wellbeing. Tansy walks alongside groups and individuals outside in nature to support them on their own journey of connection and evolution and works remotely with clients further afield. Growing up, she held a huge passion and love for dance and movement therapy and achieved a BA in Dance. Her love of working with the body and finding expression and connection with it has been rebirthed into her work with nature. Tansy leans toward a somatic approach of tending to the body through sensory and physical awareness to find guidance and enhance wellbeing. Previously a writer and presenter for Wellbeing Radio, she is deeply passionate about sharing her work with others and has a calm, grounding voice and approach to her work. She will soon release a collection of guided audio walking meditations in response to many requests from those unable to meet her in person.

In January 2021, Tansy was diagnosed with ADHD and has found nature to be an important anchor as she navigates this new layer of self-discovery. When she feels ready, she looks forward to offering more bespoke nature connection advice, content, and support to the neuro-divergent community.

To download an audio version of Tansy's tool, head to this book resource link:

https://tansyinthewild.com/sacred-spaces-audio-resource

Find and follow Tansy here: www.tansyinthewild.com

Instagram: @tansyinthewild

Facebook: www.facebook.com/tansyjanedowman

CHAPTER 10

ANCIENT PLANT WISDOM

THE KEY TO UNLEASHING YOUR SUPERNATURAL DIVINITY

Lisa Wilson, CHC

Me (a text to my husband): "I'm going to Costa Rica in July. Would you like to go?"

I had mentioned this before, and he was a solid no. I asked him, just to be polite, but fully expecting to invite my brother or sister to join me.

Perry: "Yes."

Me: "Um, did you look at the link? This is not yoga on the beach."

Perry: "Yes, I looked at it."

Me: "Are you scared?"

Perry: "Terrified."

MY STORY

With my heart pounding, I hung up the phone. I did it, something I considered for nearly a year. I studied all of the documentaries I could get my hands on. The truth is that nothing could prepare me for what I was about to embark on. Nothing. I think I still had a look of shock on my face when Joelle came in. Joelle is my right hand. She is my retreat manager, personal assistant, and business assistant. She's also become one of my very best friends.

"I did it. I booked the trip. I put down my deposit, and I made the airline reservation. There's no going back now," I said almost in a whisper.

Joelle looked stunned and excited for me at the same time. "No! Are you serious? You're actually doing this? Wow, I can't believe it."

"I know. Well, you know my motto: Do it scared. Joelle, you know I'm calling this year the year of the spirit, and yet, I don't know what is happening to me. I'm changing so fast that I can almost not keep up with myself."

And this is the exact moment in time that it hit me. It was the moment everything made sense. It was when I had one of the biggest ah-ha moments of my life. The world around me seemed to stop right there in my kitchen, for me just to take this moment in.

I spun around and looked her in the eyes. "Joelle, it's the oils. These oils are changing me. I've been doing Symphony of the Cells for months now. I'm right now realizing it's the spinal delivery to the brain and central nervous system that is literally changing me. It's the plant wisdom from around the world, changing me at the very cellular level. It's changing my thoughts, emotions, and my spirituality too."

Alright, let's back up about 15 years. I attended the Institute for Integrative Nutrition at the Jazz Center in NYC. Weekend school. It was day one, and I realized I had a raging sinus infection coming on. I recognized this familiar pain in my sinuses right away because I got them every year. Every year, I headed to my doctor and left with a prescription in hand. But here I am at school, and I can't leave. So I'm just slumped over in my chair to tough it out. I like to call those pivotal moments we all have in life "shoulder taps." This was literally a shoulder tap moment. A woman from Arizona tapped me on my shoulder:

Her: "Hey, I have a question, please. Are you open to natural solutions?"

Me: "Yes."

Her: "I have some essential oregano oil. There is a Whole Foods in the basement of this building. Oregano oil is a "hot" oil, so you will need a carrier oil. Go to the salad bar at Whole Foods. Pour one tablespoon of olive oil into a spoon. Put four drops of oregano oil in that oil. Breathe in the fumes for two to three minutes and then swallow that down. Do this four times per day."

Please understand that I had no confidence this would actually work, but at the same time, I had nothing to lose. After all, it was just oregano. I mean, I've had spaghetti before!

To my surprise, within 36 hours, I felt great. As if I had taken medicine, but I hadn't. I took "oregano."

This felt too good to be true, so I brushed it off as a mere coincidence. But I must admit that my curiosity was piqued.

When things came up, my whole family started using oregano oil, like adding to their salt gargle when they had a sore throat. My kids started discovering that this 'hot' oil did wonders for those difficult warts they picked up in the locker room. Evan would break a Q-tip in half and use that blunt edge to put the oregano oil directly onto his warts. He was thrilled by his results and thrilled that he could do this himself.

I started to consider this point: *Well, if oregano essential oils are working so well in our house, I wonder what these other oils can do?*

2007: I have my Holistic Health Coach Certificate (HHC), now what?

I graduated from the Institute of Integrative Nutrition. I was on a mission to save the world, one green smoothie at a time! I loved teaching my clients the power of clean eating and natural therapies! Admittedly, I was a tough-love coach, which was highly effective for my clients and for me. The transformation I was able to guide my clients through was blowing my mind. My health coaching practice was exploding. In fact, I usually had a several-month waitlist for those seeking to work with me.

I could not keep up with one-to-one clients, so I moved to a retreat model so I could go deep for one whole week and really offer a true reset. In 2008, I launched "The Raw Food Institute." These retreats were powerful and became award-winning retreats. People traveled in from around the world to join us.

During this week, the students got to experience state-of-the-art lectures from some of the top chefs and natural health experts in the nation. Most importantly, they got to experience a cleanse, coupled with many healing modalities.

Some of the things they did while there:

- Juice feast
- Start and end the day with wheatgrass
- Two enemas and two colon implants per day of wheatgrass or probiotics
- Two gorgeous raw, vegan meals per day
- Frequency machines / chi machine
- Vibration plates / rebounder
- Massage therapy / anti-aging facials
- Auricular therapy
- Thermography
- Healing circles
- Plant therapies / medicinal mushroom therapies such as reishi and Chaga
- Essential oils

I started bringing a physician in to teach on the topic of essential oils as therapy or medicine. This moment in time is where my journey took off. I dove deep into the study of essential oils as plant medicine, or in other words, replacing your bathroom cabinet items. I started using these oils on myself and my family. Then I started using them with my clients. This was when essential oils got really interesting for me.

Finding what I now refer to as a "miracle moment" for my clients became my new obsession. When you are a health coach, and you are coaching your client around lifestyle changes, results will come, but results do not happen overnight. What was stunning about the oils is I found a tool that created immediate results with many things, and people found this exciting! If you have something that distracts you from the life you're meant to be living, it can be really frustrating!

There are five things I like to address first with oils because the results happen fast!

1. Pain
2. Sleep
3. Digestion
4. Head tension
5. Mood

Almost everyone I work with has at least one of the issues I mentioned above. I've come to understand that oils can address most of these situations within minutes or hours. And changing just one of these items can completely change someone's life. Can you imagine having the power to change someone's life in minutes? The reason I'm so passionate about essential oils is that not only is this possible, but it happens every single day. Once just one of these issues is resolved, you have their attention. Then we can start working with the rest of the family with various challenges. By the way, oils work on many, many issues. I've just found the above five to be the extra-fast ones.

I'll never forget the day I met Aubrey. She came to one of my very first essential oil classes at The Simsbury Inn. During the class, I asked if anyone had any pain. I also asked on a scale of one-to-ten how bad the pain was, with ten being the most intense. "My knee pain is a ten," Aubrey said. In fact, on the way in, she could not even make it up one flight of stairs. She had to take the elevator. She applied a pea-size amount of Deep Blue Rub, which includes the essential oils of wintergreen, camphor, peppermint, blue tansy, German chamomile, helichrysum, ylang ylang, and osmanthus.

I wrapped up the class and walked to the front of the Inn to find Aubrey almost jogging up and down the stairs.

"Aubrey, what are you doing?" I asked. I'll never forget that great big smile on her face when she answered me. "I can't believe this is for real. When I got here, I could not make it up even one flight of stairs. But since I applied the Deep Blue Rub, I have effortlessly gone up and down several times! You don't understand. This feels like a miracle."

Hence, why I call these "miracle moments."

Helping people find their miracle moments never gets old for me. When people start getting uninterrupted sleep, their daytime energy is restored. When people have a tool to address their head tension, the relationships in their lives improve.

It cracks me up because people often think that I am the magic. I assure you, I am not the magic healer, but I do love being the bearer of the healing modality!

For years, I've had so much fun introducing people to essential oils. I love watching the expressions on their face, as they are awe-struck by the profound results in such a short period of time.

As I've been holding classes and putting oils on people, the oils were quietly working on me and working on me in the most unexpected way. While I've been nudging my own health with the oils and creating cellular health, the wisdom of the oils has been silently working its way into my consciousness. In other words, the wisdom of these plants, from the indigenous ancient wisdom of these oils, has been infusing with my DNA. It was in the kitchen with Joelle when my whole world stopped as I observed the moment in complete awe.

It was at that moment I realized that my deep desire to explore the difficult work into my soul's journey was because the oils were guiding me there.

I grew up Catholic. I went to college at a Catholic University. I love my Christian upbringing. But I felt like I was reading about mystical or profound experiences, but I had never had one personally. Yet, I craved one. I craved a supernatural experience so that I could fully connect with the Divine.

My year of the spirit began in the jungles of Costa Rica. I committed to one week with four Ayahuasca Ceremonies. Wim Hoff breath coaching, with ice baths, colon cleanses, mud baths, and daily sunrise yoga. This is the trip that took my breath away. This is the journey that will change the way I look at the world forever.

It has been my experience that the plant ceremonies that Aya can offer lift the veils and allow us to see other dimensions. Some people state they have been meditating for decades and that they get more in just one week than years of meditation can offer.

After Costa Rica, I went on to become certified in Quantum Hypnosis, retaking my spiritual insights to another level.

During the year of the spirit, I spent dedicated time to silent meditation, forest bathing, and walking barefoot on the earth.

Doing the inner work, or taking the soul's journey, makes everything better. Relationships improve. You feel free to step further into your authentic self. You have priceless, magical experiences.

Most importantly is my intuition became "spot on!" A new ability I have is my intuition kicked into high gear with stunning accuracy. When I hear something in the world, I just have to "feel into it." Admittedly, sometimes my feelings contradict what is being said. So I have to dive into research around it. Sure enough, my intuition is correct, and it has not failed me.

The plants are here to be our guides. The plants are here to offer generational wisdom from far away lands.

Plant wisdom is everywhere. From the beautiful salads we eat to the chlorophyll extractions in Green Juice Therapy. Essential oils are therapeutically powerful because of the concentrations of these plant extracts. Yet, because this immunity comes from the whole plant, essential oils can not be patented.

THE TOOL

I hope I've piqued your curiosity about essential oils.

If you are wondering how to get started with essential oils, I suggest you first get some Certified Pure Therapeutic Grade essential oils. Oils with solvents, chemicals, pesticides, and perfumes, will not only not get you a therapeutic result, they will actually make you sick. Very few oil companies in the world value purity and potency from the original indigenous regions of the earth. Know your oils.

1. Get oils

2. Get to know your oils

3. Explore them until you have your own miracle moment. Then have more miracle moments!

4. If you would like to explore the journey of your own souls, put things on the calendar that you've always wanted to do, but have not cleared time for.

5. Dedicate one full year to your very own year of the spirit — and watch the relationships in your life improve too!

If you do this, you may not recognize the beautiful human who emerges as your truest and highest self on the other side of that year.

If you have been reading the words in this chapter, and they are tugging at your soul, it is for a good reason. Everything is intentional. You're being called. You're being called to be extraordinary.

You've been "called."

Lisa Wilson is a CHC or Certified Health Coach. She is an author, speaker, entrepreneur, and mom to three earth angels.

Lisa has had the honor of speaking on some of the biggest health and wellness stages around the country, including The Raw Living Expo, The Pure Living Expo, Take Back Your Health Summit, Annie Appleseed Summit, Catch A Healthy Habit, and more.

Lisa has been taking students through one-week cleansing retreats to explore their highest human potential for over a decade. Lisa is the Founder and Owner of The Raw Food Institute. She is a Blue Diamond in DoTerra and is passionate about sharing the message of natural plant therapies + Essential Oils.

Lisa Wilson is on a life mission to explore the Journey of the Soul. She understands that the soul is sculpted over this lifetime. So we can carefully and deliberately choose activities we would like to learn and then follow the path and enjoy the soul's journey.

Lisa is living proof that you can make a living, doing what you love, and thus attract the people into your life who will collaborate with you on your biggest dreams. These people are our co-collaborators and our soul tribe.

Lisa's life philosophy is always to have an upcoming challenge to be striving for. Whether it is to write a new book, take your business to the next level, physically compete in an event, or book an adventure vacation. The excitement and preparation are most of the fun!

Lisa lives in Connecticut with her family. Her family likes pushing boundaries together! They like to do challenging hikes, explore the corners of the earth with travel, snorkel in corners of the ocean, and love with great big hearts. Most importantly, co-create the next chapter in this extraordinary life!

To find out more about Lisa, her retreats, get some (fun) essential oil education, take one of her challenges or get some oils, visit her at: lisawilsonwellness.com or visit her resource page, lisawilsonresources.com

CHAPTER 11

LIFE SHOULD BE PLAYED ON OFFENSE, NOT DEFENSE

THE BLUEPRINT FOR WINNING EVERY WEEK

Brett Eaton, Life Optimization Coach & Speaker

MY STORY

I pull into the parking spot in front of the building and continue to sit with the engine running for another five minutes. As I stare at the front door where I'll enter and spend my next ten hours, it starts to become a reality that I have no idea what awaits me inside. How many useless emails to expect, how many unimportant meetings have been scheduled, who's going to call out sick, how many times will someone else's time become more important than my own, or how many times I'll hear, "Knock, knock," "Hey Brett do you have a minute?" Naturally, everything I need to accomplish by the end of the day is now pushed to the bottom of my to-do list.

Even my personal workout is a toss-up at this point. Is that one-hour lunch break still going to exist by the time 12:30 rolls around, or will I have to end my day with a lethargic 8 pm gym sesh (which most likely I'll skip for the third day in a row)? Skipping my workout has become more commonplace these days. Oh, have I mentioned I work in the fitness industry?

For two years, I was the poster child for living life on defense. At the time, I didn't even know I was on defense since I had no idea what that really meant. However, living on defense can best be described with words like reactive, unprepared, stressed, overwhelmed, unmotivated, undisciplined, and most of all, uninspired. Simply put, living life on defense is the fast track way to un-fulfillment.

I hated Mondays because—well, they're Mondays, and well—everyone else hated Mondays. I couldn't even enjoy a Sunday without the anxiety of a looming Monday and the upcoming week creeping in to steal my Sunday's peace and joy.

As unfulfilled and lost as I felt, for some reason, I'd become easily enamored with any motivational video or speaker I happened to stumble upon on YouTube or in an ad somewhere. Something about the vibrant energy in which they spoke and the enthusiasm for life they exhibited fascinated me.

One day, a friend sent me a podcast. It was one of the first podcasts I'd ever listened to. Podcasts were fairly new, and I had no real interest in them. This one, however, turned out to be a game-changer for me. The host and his guest spent almost an hour discussing the reasons why routines and boundaries are critical for success, and why success isn't random, it's planned.

Normally, I would have given it a listen and moved on; however, for some reason, that day, it stopped me in my tracks and consumed my every thought. Not only could I not stop thinking about it, but it catapulted me into this obsession with learning, researching, and studying the most motivated and successful people in the world. How did they reach the level they're at? What did they do every single day? What do they think about? What questions do they ask themselves? How do they plan their day? How did they generate enthusiasm for life as opposed to the everyday person just trying to get through the day?

Over the next two years, this obsession continued as I spent every morning listening to a motivational video or podcast. Every day without fail, I started my day with a video or podcast that could get me one step closer to becoming more like the people I was listening to and watching that day.

People often say knowledge is power. Believe it or not, I disagree. My two years of daily listening taught me that all the knowledge in the world wouldn't change a thing. So it's not actually in the knowledge but in implementing that knowledge where the power lies. Knowledge is only potential power.

It was in those daily video and podcast lessons that it became extremely clear to me what the biggest difference was for the most successful, highest performers who seemed like they had 25 or 26 hours in their day.

I know, I know, you're ready for the damn secret, right?

Okay, here it is.

They planned.

Yeah, I thought the same thing too. *No way. That was it? That's the big secret?*

It had to be sexier and more complicated than that, right? Well, it wasn't. That was the common difference-maker. People who consistently got more done properly planned to get more done. They planned for their success and fully expected to have great days, to get a lot done, and entered their weeks expecting to dominate.

Once I learned this, I began combining everything I learned with techniques I used for years of helping clients stick to their workout and eating schedules. While doing this, I created my own planning process that got me out of the repetitive weekly funk of just surviving and hanging on for dear life until the weekend.

Over the next few years, this process would completely change my life. However, that's not even the best part. It began to change other people's lives because I started teaching it! This process took me from an unfulfilled personal trainer and fitness manager to a passion-driven life coach helping hundreds of people create the habits and routines needed to squeeze every drop out of life. I was finally playing offense.

I believe life is meant to be played on offense. When I say offense, I mean in control, prepared, on your terms, confident, and disciplined. Back in my fitness days, I coined the phrase, "You can't dominate your week without dominating your day. Just like you can't dominate your day without dominating your morning." Today, I would take that phrase one step further and add that you can't dominate your morning if you aren't armed with a specific and organized plan of attack.

This is exactly why I created this planning process. This simple tool will have you getting more done, predictably, every single week. No matter what your life currently looks like, this planning process will have you feeling more effective and efficient with your time than ever before.

Dwight D. Eisenhower once said, "Plans are nothing. Planning is everything." He couldn't have been more accurate. We all *think* we have a plan when we wake up on Monday. However, if that plan solely exists in your head, then it's still messy, unorganized, and cluttered. Once you get it down on paper and into a schedule, now it can be cleaned up. Now scheduling conflicts can be avoided. Commitments can be prioritized. Even date night can find its specific place. It's all about being prepared, organized, and fully in control of the week you're about to step into.

Sounds great, Brett, but the last thing I want to do is spend the last hours of my Sunday night planning out my week. Well, guess what? *I agree.*

Sunday night is a terrible time to plan. Nobody wants to be thinking about work on a Sunday night when you're desperately trying to soak up the last remaining hours of the weekend. The ironic thing is, by that time, due to the lack of planning and preparation, most people are already thinking about Monday and the upcoming week. Why? Because they know they're unprepared. Just like I was, sitting in my car outside the building, dreading my walk in.

What if there was a way that you could enjoy Sunday night while feeling calm, confident, and relaxed that Monday was going to be great. What if you already knew that all your important obligations and commitments were planned and organized in your calendar at a dedicated and specific time. Date night, family dinner, workout, morning routine, calls, meetings, and to-do list were already set perfectly.

Yeah, that would be freaking awesome, Brett.

You're damn right it would!

Would you believe me if I told you that 30 minutes of Sunday planning was the only thing preventing you from becoming one of those high-performing successful people I referenced earlier?

The bottom line is that life is meant to be played on offense. Those who play offense win the game of life. Although that may look different for each person, those who consistently live on defense react and conform to others while watching them succeed.

Ask yourself right now, have you been playing offense or defense lately?

Are you planned, prepared, proactive, and consistently sticking to your commitments and moving the needle in your life every week? Have you been playing offense?

Or, have you felt unorganized, unplanned, reactive, and consistently setting goals and commitments that fall short and keep getting pushed from week to week, month to month, and year to year? Have you been playing defense?

No matter where you are currently, planning to *Win-The-Week* is the best way to achieve more, see more results, and do it more effectively and efficiently than ever.

You deserve to win! We all do! And the only way to win the game of life is by playing offense.

THE TOOL

THE BLUEPRINT FOR WINNING EVERY WEEK

Now we know how vital planning is in order for us to play offense. But how exactly do we plan a whole week without it taking hours?

I can promise you it will only take 30 minutes each week to plan the entire upcoming week. By setting up your week, you'll save countless hours and avoid daily decision fatigue. This process will walk you through steps needed to prioritize important tasks, follow through with your weekly commitments, and become a master of your to-do list. This process alone can completely change your life.

Okay, are you ready to become a high-performing, successful individual?

Here are the eight steps that will consistently have you prepared and set up to *Win-The-Week*:

Step 1. A Setting For Success: Create an environment that makes you excited to prepare for your success this upcoming week. This can be in your office, your favorite room in your house, your backyard, your favorite chair, or at your favorite coffee shop. Ask yourself when is the most effective time on Sunday for you to plan? Will it be handwritten or digital? What music and lighting might help you focus and concentrate? How will you feel knowing your whole week is planned for success? I encourage you to choose a place and time that is repeatable each week. This will make it easier for this to become a habit.

PRO TIP: I already reiterated that Sunday night is *not* the best time for this setup. I recommend Sunday *morning*, perhaps while you drink your morning coffee or right after breakfast. Distraction-free in an environment that gets you excited for your weekly success.

Step 2. Choose A Reward: You need to have a reward planned for completing your setup. This is an often overlooked step because it's easy to convince yourself that you don't need a reward for something you should be doing anyway. However, setting up your week is something only a very small percentage of people do. As humans, when we're rewarded for something, we're more likely to want to do it again. Examples could include spending time watching football, ordering from your favorite restaurant, or spending time at the pool.

PRO TIP: This 30-minute exercise will save you hours each week and reduce thousands of decisions, so you're damn right; you deserve a reward!

Step 3. Review: Imagine this section as watching the game film from your previous week. A chance to look back and learn from our miscues and any poor decisions so we can learn the lesson to prevent repeating those miscues. Questions to consider: What is the biggest area of opportunity you can take away from last week? What is the one thing you'd go back over and do differently if you could? How can you be better prepared if this happens again?

PRO TIP: Focus on one constructive thing instead of beating yourself up by pointing out all your mistakes. Remember, we are learning a lesson here to prevent it from recurring, so try your best to keep it positive.

Step 4. Scan For Landmines: This is my personal favorite step during the setup because of how crucial it has been for my own pre-planning. You're going to review your calendar for the upcoming two weeks. The idea here is to search for any potential *landmines* or things that could blow up your week and derail your momentum. Most landmines can be avoided with a bit of future planning and awareness. Some landmines may require you to reschedule calls or meetings, move workouts, change meal times, or plan for travel. Identify social events, holidays, big meetings, travel, or anything that may alter your normal daily routine. Now, proactively make any changes necessary so that you're still in control of as much of your week as possible.

PRO TIP: Scanning for landmines will keep you proactive with any and all changes to your normal schedule and routines. Only look at the upcoming two weeks ahead to prevent feeling overwhelmed.

Step 5. Commitments: Ideally, you have already set some quality goals for the month, quarter, or year and are using those larger goals here to set a leveraged weekly commitment. I believe all commitments should begin with *I will* instead of:

I'll try to. . .

I'll do my best to. . .

Maybe I can. . .

I should be able to. . .

Hopefully, I can. . .

All of those still feel optional. "*I will*," on the other hand, is a strong declarative statement. One that feels like the action is already done. Think about it, would you feel more confident if I told you, "Maybe I can make it to the airport to pick you up," or if I said, "I will be there to pick you up." Our brain hears the *"I will"* statement confidently and with conviction. Commitments can't be negotiable. If they're negotiable, they're still in the decision phase, and not yet a commitment. Make sure the commitment is in your control only.

PRO TIP: Make them realistic and as crystal clear and specific as possible. A friend should be able to complete your commitment without any further questions. If they still have questions, then *you* still have questions, and therefore your commitment is not specific enough.

Step 6. Prioritize Your To-Do List: Time to add anything new to your weekly to-do list. As easy as it is to add, be sure to delete non-essential tasks and delegate any tasks that can be completed by someone other than you. Just include things you intend on doing *this week only*. On the left side of your notebook (or below if you're using a digital version), you can keep a *long-term to-do list* for anything you need to do but is not urgent for this week. Do not overload your week with unrealistic expectations. Fight the urge to put down everything that needs to get done, and stick to things that must be completed this week. Everything else can go on the other side of the page on your *long-term to-do list*.

PRO TIP: Get comfortable with a smaller *this-week-only* to-do list so you begin the habit of checking off the entire list, rather than a long to-do list that you only get halfway through. High performers are finishers. This will help you set realistic expectations and follow through at a much higher frequency.

Step 7. Schedule It: Block off specific time on your calendar for each task on your to-do list and schedule all commitments. This step alone can increase your chances of accomplishing tasks by 30%. Be as realistic as you can and lean towards overestimating the time you expect each task to take. *Breaking news*: it won't all fit. This is precisely why you need to prioritize, delete, delegate, and move tasks over to your long-term to-do list. Each week contains 168 hours. Assuming eight hours of sleep a night, that leaves you with 112 hours. Take extreme ownership over those hours and use them as wisely as you can. Be sure to prioritize family, fun, and self-care. Be sure to block off specific times for your morning, evening, and other self-care routines.

PRO TIP: It will seem easy to skip this step or to only schedule half of your commitments or to-do list items. However, this is by far the most impactful step. Having a specific, blocked-off time to complete each task is the only way to ensure you completely own your schedule and are living life on offense.

Step 8. Enjoy Your Reward: Celebrating this process makes you that much more likely to repeat it again next week. Celebrating the small wins gets you more excited for big wins. I tell my clients that "If you don't celebrate the small wins, you often don't get the opportunity to celebrate the big wins."

PRO TIP: Be sure to notice how your "Sunday Scaries" and anxiety levels for the upcoming week tend to dissipate now that you're set up and prepared. Feels pretty good, huh? Almost like we should do this again next week!

I hope you found my story and this tool of planning helpful and insightful. I truly believe you owe it to yourself to live your life on offense because you deserve to win the game of life. Winning takes planning, and planning takes action. I cannot wait to hear how this *Win-The-Week* setup has changed your life.

If you could use more support with your setup, I'd like to invite you to check out the following link, where you'll find the *Win-The-Week* training. Complete with a digital copy of the workbook, I walk you through each step with a training video. There's even an option to add on two calls with me to ensure you master your weekly setup process! Please visit https://brett-eaton.mykajabi.com/wintheweek to continue your journey to a life lived on offense!

Brett Eaton is a Life Optimization Coach, speaker, author, owner, and founder of *The Better You Blueprint Coaching Program*, and co-host of the podcast *The Better You Blueprint Podcast*.

Brett received his Bachelor's Degree in Kinesiology-Exercise Science and has worked with clients all over the world through training and now coaching for over 15 years. He has spoken at events and to companies all over the country, motivating and inspiring people to optimize their productivity, routines, habits, and overall fulfillment.

Brett believes life is meant to be played on offense, not defense. His goal is to help as many people as he can play offense in their life by creating a life they are excited about. Brett's superpower is helping men and women identify and prioritize their professional goals and align them with their personal interests to create the life they truly want.

With the perfect mix of encouragement and tough love, Brett knows exactly how to get people from wishing, wanting, and waiting to prioritizing goals, taking action, sticking to daily and weekly commitments, and reaching the next level of success. Brett thrives on inspiring and impacting people to ask better questions, dig deeper, break out of their comfort zone, and create new standards for their life.

For more of Brett's content, you can follow him on Instagram @motivatedByBrett, Linked In @ Brett Eaton, or on his Podcast, the *Better You Blueprint Podcast*.

Visit www.facebook.com/groups/1820650791558166 to join his free Facebook community. To learn more about Brett's Coaching Programs, or hire him to speak to your team, please visit www.MotivatedByBrett.com.

CHAPTER 12

OVERCOMING INVISIBILITY AND SELF-DOUBT

YOU DESERVE TO BE SEEN

Jen Griswold

MY STORY

I wore the long, zoned-out stare of an exhausted mom. My husband was on another Air Force trip. I lost count of how many days I was home alone that year. He missed my daughter's first two birthdays. At times I wondered if she mistook the nice guy across the street who always played with her for her dad. That particular day, I looked across the room, which was littered with Duplo Legos and Matchbox cars. Both kids were dressed in only a diaper, with their soft and innocent rolls looking a little grey. I could smell the rancid scent of one needing to be changed. All of us were fighting a nasty virus and moving slow.

My three-year-old son moaned, "Mommaaaa, I don't feel good. I think my bum just threw up!" I laugh at his toddler honesty now, but I was paralyzed with emptiness then. I didn't have it in me to move, much less take care of another human. I was exhausted, sick of my situation, and alone. The weight of my loneliness made me feel like I could fade into the drab color of the worn carpet. I thought to myself, *motherhood is supposed to be one of the best times of life, but I am numb inside right now. I used to have goals and dreams and the motivation to achieve them. Is this all I'm destined to do for the rest of my life? There has to be more.*

As messy and miserable as I was at the time, it became an anchoring moment I've returned to over and over again because, as hard as it was, I gained so much clarity from it. It was in that destitute moment on the floor that I made a conscious decision to change my situation. I resolved to begin the journey to find the "old me" again. To rediscover the girl who had confidence in her own skin, ran after her visions, and had a purpose for life bigger than the groundhog's day that was slowly breaking me.

A CULTURE OF INVISIBILITY

You could easily dismiss my story as one of a classic, overwhelmed mom dealing with a lot of time alone with her kids. But, there was more to it. My numb state of mind was reached by years of cumulative gut punches that accompanied our military life. Prior to motherhood, I was a confident woman with a proud list of achievements. I was the high school's valedictorian, an Air Force Academy distinguished graduate, and a volleyball walk-on. I had a master's degree by the age of 23, and I left active duty as a Captain in the Air Force in a historically male-dominated career field (Aircraft Maintenance). But when I became a military spouse, it felt like my former identity or achievements were irrelevant and useless. I sensed a pressure to assimilate to the unwritten rule; spouses sacrifice their careers to support their military members. And I slowly began to believe the best way to survive was to do what most spouses did, succumb to the heavy reality that I was now an invisible supporter of my military husband. Additionally, we would move every two to three years, which made maintaining a career path very challenging, if not impossible. The outlook for finding a way out of this situation was grim.

As I researched work possibilities that would fit with my experience managing hundreds of troops and an extensive academic pedigree, it was shocking to find out that there were very few part-time work options for me. In fact, while doing research, I discovered 90% of military spouses reported wanting to work. Yet, they were still under or unemployed with a jobless rate of three times the national average. So, I thought to myself, *I could roll over and accept that fate, or I could forge a new path, think outside the box, find my purpose and be the pioneer that would forge new options for these resilient and impressive spouses.*

SCARED TO HIRE YOURSELF?

I grew up as a child of entrepreneurs. My parents' home office was in the bedroom next to mine. I remember laying my head down on many nights during high school, watching my parents burn the midnight oil so they could spend day hours attending my athletic events. Given that the part-time job market was grim, and I was the primary parent at home, I began thinking about entrepreneurship for myself. I pondered, *I had skills like my parents, right? Was it possible I could provide something of value to others and make a living?* It was time to find out.

But going outside the norm is not encouraged in our military community, where standardization and similarity are prized. So, the thought of it was slightly terrifying. *What will people think of me? What will my family say? Will I jeopardize my husband's career? Will they understand that I don't fit into the traditional culture of stay-at-home moms and doting spouses? Will anyone relate to the deep need I have to forge a new path?* In order to overcome the natural voices in my head, I knew I needed to be grounded in a deep sense of who I was, what purpose I'd serve, and why I wanted to take the road less traveled.

One of my biggest fears, when I began toying with the idea of entrepreneurship, was that people would misconstrue my intentions as being selfish and only for the purpose of making me more money. When it was so much more than that, it was about finding myself, serving something bigger, and helping others in a way that would help me feel fulfilled, valued, appreciated, and whole again.

So I began a quest to find my purpose and the perfect business to execute it. I knew I needed to clearly define what I was seeking in order to be ready to tackle my own self-doubts and the barrage of questions that would most certainly arise from others. As I progressed, I found one particular tool that helped me time and time again.

THE TOOL

A CLEAR PURPOSE STATEMENT

Once I decided to start my first business, I did all the things that eager, new entrepreneurs do. I bought business cards, created my own website, printed beautiful stationery, and strategized where to advertise my services in order to get off to a strong start. I also began nervously telling people about my services. But on my first attempts, I felt unsure and audibly stumbled over my words. Having a background in the military and zero experience marketing anything before (much less myself), I felt a bit like a used car salesman every time I would try.

But the more I studied the tenets of marketing, the more I realized I needed a quick and concise "elevator pitch" to answer the common question, "What do you do?" Yet, I had trouble coming up with the right words. The only thing that rolled off my tongue effortlessly was my own story. It flowed easily and had a natural, authentic feel, which often captivated anyone to whom I was talking. But when I'd get to the part of my story where I began to explain what I did, I would end up droning on too long and leaving people confused.

Thankfully, early in my business, I had a respected mentor candidly ask me, "Why did you choose to go into business for yourself?" It was a simple question, but one that left me perplexed and sleepless for a few nights as my mind yearned for an explanation. *Why was I moved to choose this path?* My mentor pointed out that I could have landed a traditional job with a very respectable income with all my experience. But I knew it wasn't about the money for me. I was sure of that.

When I dreamed about the future, I always felt my energy swell when I envisioned the change I could create, the women I could inspire, and the good I could do in my community. In the midst of one of those swells, it finally hit me! I sprung out of bed, ran downstairs, stumbling through the dark house, and grabbed my laptop. I began typing my string of thoughts furiously as I banged at the keys. Several paragraphs later, I underlined the main theme, "I'm starting a business so I can make an impact on women who feel left behind!" That sentence created visceral energy inside me that continues to drive me deeply to this day. Years after this initial late-night brainstorm, I continued to write an entire book titled *Mission Entrepreneur: Applying Lessons from Military Life to Create Success in Business Startups.*

After a lot of trial and error, I concluded that it was a combination of my authentic story *and* the clear impact I provided with my services that allowed me to get my purpose across in my own, non-sales version of the traditional elevator pitch. It was concise and straightforward. And it sounded something like this:

"Like most military spouses, after years of struggling to find a traditional job that fit my needs, I realized I'd never find that 'magic job,' and I needed to create my own. So, I started my own business.

Fast forward 11 years. I've helped thousands of other women go from unfulfilled and under or unemployed to empowered and thriving by coaching them how to start and run their own flexible businesses so they can support themselves and their families without sacrificing income-producing careers or their home life."

THE FORMULA

The formula to create your purpose statement is simple, and it helps you identify seven key pieces of your client's journey that'll help them quickly and easily understand the value you provide. The following is the general formula your purpose statement will take:

{Short backstory highlighting pain point}, I realized that {mission/ passion/light bulb moment}. I help {ideal client} go from {original state to desired outcome} by {what you offer} without {negative stress/state} so they can {transformed emotional state}.

In this two-sentence formula, you'll walk your listener through the journey they will take if they decide to work with you.

First, begin by giving a quick summary of the backstory that led you to create the business, products, or services you provide. What was the specific struggle or pain point that you overcame to get to your current state, and what was the epiphany you experienced that led to a new mission, passion, or light bulb moment that helped you to think differently? Make sure you specifically identify and describe your ideal client so there is no confusion. What age and gender are they? Where do they live? What needs do they have?

Next, what can your ideal client expect to experience in terms of a transformation after working with you? Describe what undesirable state they began in originally and the transformation to the desired outcome or state of mind you strive for them to achieve. Then, describe the product or service you offer to get them a new and better outcome. If your offer has a time frame (three-day course, one-hour meditation, five-step plan), be sure to state it.

Transformations are best understood when you remind your ideal client of the pain holding them back. In this section, you'll want to clearly describe the negative outcomes and pitfalls you'll help them avoid. Finally, leave your ideal client excited at the idea of gaining a new emotional state or way of thinking after working with you! Allow your listener to feel the emotional high of seeing their better future by the end of your purpose statement.

Once you've assembled your statement to your liking, put it all together and say it out loud at least five times to see how it flows. If you need more help or you don't feel like you like this format, I encourage you to check out some other options at my resource link at www.bossladybio.com/jengriswold to try out three other purpose statement formats my company offers to help you find the right fit.

Here are a few additional examples to follow:

EXAMPLE: After seven years in corporate law while trying to become a law partner, be a good mom and wife, and have it all, I was burned out. Big time. I discovered that I was chasing someone else's dream and realized that there's another way to have it all. I now help other women escape unfulfilling corporate careers so they can create sustainable home-based businesses without giving up income or their happiness so they can thrive again.

EXAMPLE: When I first started in business, I was a hot mess when it came to money management and organization until I figured out simple tricks to get me on track. Now I help overwhelmed small business owners go from being numbers haters with receipts stuffed in shoeboxes to happy and organized by teaching them my easy bookkeeping system in less than three weeks.

PUT IT INTO PRACTICE

Okay, so now that you've identified and curated your purpose statement, it's time to put it into practice. Once you're confident and have practiced it, you'll be amazed at how often you'll find an opportunity to use it to create connections.

My favorite example of using my purpose statement happened on a day when I was *way* outside my comfort zone. I was fortunate enough to be invited to a luncheon in Washington DC with some of the city's most prominent CEOs, connectors, and politicos. During the luncheon, a renowned local philanthropist was scheduled to interview the U.S. Secretary of the Treasury. As honored as I was to receive the invitation, I immediately felt my stomach tense up, envisioning how I would fit in amongst this room full of powerful players. I mean, I work from home coaching women over Zoom. That means you'll usually find me dressed in yoga pants and a tee-shirt or ripped jeans and a messy bun. Not exactly the look they'd be going for at this professional event. But this was an opportunity that might only come around once, so despite my sweaty palms, I hesitantly said yes.

Once I accepted the invitation, I began tackling my anxiety about what to wear. I knew the default outfit in DC was a grey, navy, or black suit for men or the equivalent dress or pantsuit for women. I owned nothing of the sort and had no interest in purchasing something I'd never wear again, so I reminded myself of my purpose (to serve women) and decided to dress exactly as I normally would if I were meeting a room full of my ideal clients. After considering several color choices, I picked a striking, black and white collared shift dress with large pink poppies in stripes around the bodice. I added a bright pink Zara overcoat with sleek cat-eye sunglasses and a coordinating handbag. Think Elle Woods crossed with Olivia Pope from Scandal.

When I walked into the Ritz Carlton ballroom, I felt as out of place as my bright pink jacket looked in the sea of drab suits. I sat down at my assigned seat next to seven others and immediately began inventing stories in my mind about how these men were more worthy than me to be here. By then, the sweat on my palms had traveled to my armpits and forehead as well. As I listened to everyone introduce themselves and give their elevator pitch, I realized we all had ties to the military community. When it was my turn, my knees began shaking, and a hot flush came over my face. But once

I began talking, the familiarity of my purpose statement took over, and the words flowed freely.

Stuffy suited man: "So, Jen, what do you do?"

Me: "Like most military spouses, after years of struggling to find a traditional job that fit my needs, I realized that I'd never find that 'magic job,' and I needed to create my own. So I started my own business. Fast forward eleven years, I've helped thousands of other women go from unfilled and under or unemployed to empowered and thriving by coaching them how to start and run their own flexible businesses so they can support themselves and their families without sacrificing income-producing careers or their home life."

What happened next absolutely blew my mind. For the remainder of the luncheon, the object of our entire table's attention was me. Yes, me! The nervous one who didn't think she fit in or belonged at the table. My inquisitive table mates took turns asking me questions about the story of my business and how I achieved success. They marveled at the number of women I had coached. They requested my card to meet up, they listed people they wanted to introduce me to, and they were inspired by how I was determined to improve the unemployment statistics in the military spouse community.

By the end of the event, my strong upright body language and bold hand gestures told an entirely different story than when I first walked in. As we said our goodbyes, I jumped in my Uber and let out an audible squeal once the door was closed. *Eeek! What in the world just happened?* As I replayed the whole event in my mind, it hit me; *my purpose statement conveyed my message and struck a chord with everyone!* Not only did it resonate with my audience effectively, but it gave me the confidence I needed to realize that I deserved to be at that table just as much as the next guy.

So whether you're just starting out and sharing your purpose statement for the first time, or you're seasoned and looking for confidence in owning your worthiness, your purpose statement is something you'll revisit again and again. Use it as your rally cry to remind yourself that you deserve to be seen and heard, you have what it takes to get out there and share your gifts with the world, and you-yes, you-deserve a seat at the table!

Jen Griswold is an entrepreneur, author, and retired military officer with a heart for serving her community through teaching entrepreneurship and providing marketing resources to women.

After a successful 20 year career in the Air Force, Jen now leads the training, development, and production of a distributed team of over 9,000 entrepreneurs that produces over $10M in skincare sales annually. She has been featured on the Today Show, in Arlington Magazine, NextGenMilspouse, and on a variety of podcasts about entrepreneurship and performance.

In 2017, Jen published her solo book, *Mission Entrepreneur*, and started a marketing and branding company with the same name. Mission Entrepreneur recently launched its hottest new product, BossLady Bio, a marketing tool that turns the link in your social media bio into a powerful mini-site for free. She is excited to be able to democratize women's access to websites with this tool.

Jen lives in Arlington, Virginia, with her husband Kevin, their two children, and a delightful rescue dog. When she's not working at her laptop or sitting on the sidelines of sporting events, you can find her running the scenic trails of the DC area.

You can find more about Jen and her latest adventures and offerings at her resource link: www.bossladybio.com/jengriswold

CHAPTER 13

AWAKING THE TEMPLE

HOW TO BUILD A FOUNDATION OF ARETE—EXCELLENCE

Dr. Sam Pappas, MD

"Man blames nature for his fate, yet his fate is mostly an echo of his character, passions, mistakes, and weaknesses."

~Democritus.

MY STORY

"Doc, you're an orphaned adult."

The crisp fall morning vibrated with promise as leaves rustled in the background and ten-year-old boys rhythmically exhorted each other on the nearby soccer field. The words of the soccer dad and armchair psychologist behind me hung over my head like lingering smoke from a pipe.

"Joyce told us, I'm sorry to hear about the loss of your father. Like me, you are an orphaned adult."

Bruce's analysis then hit me like a thunderbolt and broke me out of my trance. He proceeded to empathize with my current plight, for he, too lost both of his parents. Over the next 20 minutes, he shared how he took a deep dive into this topic. He overcame his battle with grief caused by the underappreciated challenges we middle-aged adults can face with the loss of both parents.

"You are left with this empty feeling and void in your core."

In retrospect, Bruce's words were like manna from heaven and started me on my path to reset my mindset and springboard into a better version of myself. But initially, this was uncharted territory for me.

As an internal medicine doctor who specializes in integrative health and wellness, I spend my day discussing these important matters with patients—taking the time not only to find out the what but, more importantly, the why of what ails a person. But clearly, I wasn't taking the time to properly assess my current state, as Socrates said, "first know thyself."

From afar, things looked good. I had been in practice for over five years in Northern Virginia and had made a successful new beginning after uprooting my wife and two-year-old son from a stressful five years in my homeland of New Jersey. I was blessed to have a growing practice where appreciative patients enjoyed a doctor taking his time to really get to know them. I was slowly building a good reputation and realized I was making significant strides when my new patient told me; you're being called 'The Doctor Oz of Arlington' by the Mothers of North Arlington support group.

"See what happens when you understand that the smartest person in the room is a women's intuition." Joyce was correct as usual.

I reclaimed my prior good health after being in the wilderness, physically and spiritually, during my residency. I realized the cumulative years of stressful medical training, including poor sleep, lack of sunlight, reduced physical activity, and a brown diet reminiscent of most college boys took me far away from my healthy Greek American foundation. As the author and intuitive healer Carolyn Myss has said, "Your biography becomes your biology."

After my residency, I returned to New Jersey with my new wife but was left in an insufficient state to optimally handle an unraveling situation. Mom was diagnosed with ovarian cancer at the young age of 50. Dad's 'broken heart' at seeing his wife slowly succumb to her disease compounded by my younger brother's worsening mental health problems wore on his formerly resilient core.

My years of traditional medical training and academic knowledge proved unable to provide an adequate compass and add meaningful value to my parent's declining health beyond taking a pill to match the ill.

Initially, this crisis spurred me onward and upward. With the help of my wife, I sought a path of more meaning and a deepening faith which then triggered a pursuit of a comprehensive understanding of real health and wellness, what Hippocrates called *positive health*. I vigorously pursued and applied lessons learned from the study of the Greek origins of health. This was not only in its ancient forms but also in the amazing data emerging on the resiliency and longevity of the post World War II and pre-industrial age peasant farmers of Greece.

I learned that a healthy mind, body, and spirit could be nurtured or tuned via rigorous physical exercise, strict diet, regular study of ethics and character, and a daily practice of contemplating the *cosmos* for a deeper understanding of philosophy and faith.

"You are adrift." I was surprised at Joyce's assessment of my impromptu therapy session on the soccer fields of Northern Virginia. She tactfully but firmly agreed that as an orphaned adult, I was slowly going off course. She laid out that I had a false sense of completeness with my family situation.

We helped my father take care of my mom's last days with hospice. We also set up my younger brother in a group home so that my father could try to mend his health. He stubbornly refused to be with us and slowly succumbed to progressive heart and kidney problems before passing away a few years later. I was grateful for our time together but had not really thought about what all of this meant.

"I think your mindset is off." When I further asked my better half what I needed to do, she did her best Cher impersonation from the movie Moonstruck imploring me, like Nicholas Cage, to "snap out of it." Fortunately, without the multiple slaps to the face.

When the pupil is ready, the teacher appears.

When I opened myself up to the possibility that I needed a different outlook, many things appeared before me to set me on a better path. We all need signposts on our journey for a better direction.

"We become more whole when we recognize that we are incomplete. Only when we confess the hole in our soul can we be filled to overflowing."

~Father John Chryssavgis - *Soul Mending.*

The random book I picked up at the library by children's noted author Shel Silverstein had deeper meanings. *The Missing Piece* tells the story of a circle that, while whole, rolled at a rapid pace and missed many things. But when incomplete, they traveled slowly and rejoiced that they enjoyed every scenery.

I found noted psychologist and expert on meaning Alex Pattakos' book, *The OPA Way*, full of insight. His words on arete (excellence) as a virtue imbibed by Greek villagers full of resiliency particularly struck home.

It felt like Alex was personally speaking to me and imploring a fellow tribe member to live with arete and purpose.

"Our inner world, to a large degree, controls our outer world. Our mental attitude becomes our personality and the lens which we view the world, which, in turn, influences how we live. To improve our conditions, we must first improve ourselves."

And finally, when looking for material to augment my son's classroom assignment, I found a paper encouraging me to be more of an ancient Athenian.

Author and cultural critic, Neil Postman, wrote an article of a graduation speech he never gave but would have, he said, if given the opportunity, entitled *Athenians and Visigoths - How to Quell Your Inner Barbarian.* He compares these two cultures whose way of looking at the world remains with us. They both still survive, and they do so through us and the ways in which we conduct our lives.

The Athenians were believed to contemplate, reason, and experiment with the most exalted activities a person can perform. They held knowledge, and especially the quest of knowledge, in high esteem. They prepared their imagination through learning and experience and valued discipline and skill. The Athenians placed great value on tradition, social restraint, and continuity, for the thread which holds civilized society together is thin and vulnerable. Most importantly of all, Postman believed that anyone could be an Athenian.

I found that I could awaken my inner temple. Both in St. Paul's words to the Corinthians, your body is the temple of the Holy Spirit and of the Asclepian temples, the Ancient Greek healing sanctuaries, and forerunners of our modern-day spas.

I put all of this together and created a roadmap to hit the brakes on my drifting and forge a better foundation. It is these principles that I use to help someone reorient their mindset to achieve excellence or *arete*.

THE TOOL

"Knowing yourself is the beginning of all wisdom."

~Aristotle.

1. Telos: Purposeful end or goal

In her book *Thrive*, Arianna Huffington describes how her uneducated Greek mother presided over her and her sister for long sessions in their small kitchen in Athens, discussing timeless principles on how to live a good life. As Arianna describes it, "Philosophy for the Greeks was not an academic exercise, it was a way of life. A daily practice in the art of living." As Socrates said over 2000 years ago, "An unexamined life is not worth living."

Traditional cultures are enlivened by a philosophical mindset that imbues an ethos of purpose and meaning, where a personal code and responsibility are examined and articulated. They have an end or purpose in mind, a telos.

Telos is a Greek word used by both Greek philosophers and religious writers and means a purpose, goal, intent, or an ultimate result of an event.

According to the Theology of Work blog, "when you know where things are going, you can orient yourself toward that end. If you don't know that future, your life can become extremely off course. A trustworthy vision of the future acts as a compass, orienting us to where we are going so that we can continue to head that way. Our praxis, the things we do daily, are then fashioned in light of that orientation."

This future-thinking mindset is best established through self-examination and contemplation. Ancient Greek thinkers were influenced by the cults of Pythagoras and Orpheus and practiced daily walks in nature to contemplate the cosmos.

Monks from the East to the West have been practicing silence, simplicity, and solitude for thousands of years to first "know thyself." St. Basil, a fourth-century AD theologian trained in ancient Greek philosophy and Christian thought, established the first-ever rules for monks. He believed there should be both daily contemplation and self-examination.

Today we moderns no longer live under a sacred canopy as any fulfillment we possess derives from things we possess. Our modern-day philosopher Arianna points to poet Mark Nepo's definition of sacrifice: "Giving up with reverence and compassion what no longer works, in order to stay close to what is sacred." This can then be used as a place to begin thinking about sacrificing which habits don't work.

Make sacred time to withdraw and nurture your soul and spirit so that you can examine, critique, and unleash your innate purposefulness or *telos* with worthy goals while saying no to lesser goals.

"Only the educated are free."

~Epictetus.

2. The gymnasium of virtue: education, and character determines fate.

Plato's Academy, which taught both men and women, was the first institution of higher learning and embraced the principles of beautiful souls in strong bodies. As a forerunner of the famous gymnasiums, it was believed that intellectual pursuits and character development had equal importance with physical health and training.

It was believed that a proper molding of one's character required a sound education. The ancient Greeks believed the skills of achieving excellence in life or arete could be taught and learned, and one was free to expand his opportunities through education. Luke Timothy Johnson states that the wonderfully elusive word "Paideia" means both education and culture. This concept embodied the ideals or principles of a society that was passed down from generation to generation.

Plutarch, the famous biographer of Greek and Roman lives and who Shakespeare based many of his stories on, believed one could create character traits by studying the habits and actions of famous lives. In effect, one could learn about ethics and virtue from these stories and develop a plan of what to do and not to do in striving for improvement.

Plato separated virtues into both *physical* (health, strength, and beauty) and *ethical* (piety, temperance, courage, and justice). Aristotle tells us that virtue is excellence or arete at being human. The virtues are powers or moral habits that enable us to be what we ought to be.

Traditional cultures have routinely embodied wisdom in how to live by highlighting habits and virtue.

Of all the aphorisms on character and virtue that were passed down to us from the ancient Greeks, the most important for our mindset may be *nothing in excess*. Along with the phrase *know thyself*, it holds a special place in sayings found throughout cities established by Alexander the Great when he conquered much of the modern-day Middle East and Central Asia and helped spread many of the tenets of Hellenic wisdom. This is not a call for mediocrity but an understanding of the danger of extremes.

Nothing in excess has been called a fitting description of the virtue of temperance or sophrosyne, which Aristotle described as having appetites "for the right things, in the right ways, at the right times."

Sophrosyne is often described as self-control or wise moderation but can also be considered good sense or sound-mindedness.

Wikipedia explains the definition and its cross-cultural significance:

"Sophrosyne is an ancient Greek concept of an ideal of excellence of character and soundness of mind. When combined in one well-balanced individual leads to other qualities, such as temperance, moderation, prudence, purity, decorum, and self-control. It is similar to the concepts of Zhongyong of Chinese Confucianism and Sattva of Indian thought."

Create or forge rather than find a personal code of habits that embodies self-mastery. Focus on sound-mindedness and self-control as a duty and obligation to not only yourself but to your loved ones and sphere of influence.

"He who learns must suffer. Even in our sleep, pain which cannot forget falls drop by drop upon the heart, until in our own despair, against our will, comes wisdom through the awful grace of God."

~Aeschylus

3. Agon: Embrace the struggle.

For the Greeks, life was a struggle and a competition. Stories of those overcoming adversity abound in their myths and lore. Homeric warriors delighted in grievous contests, and the poet Pindar described an athlete as one "who delights in the toil and cost."

My twin brother Tom and I often use the word *corporate athlete* in counseling both men and women in the concept of the daily struggle for excellence in the workforce and in life. The term athlete in the original meaning denoted both a contest and the prize of the contest. This contest always involved effort and struggle or *agon*.

Noted C.S. Lewis scholar Louis Markos has further highlighted this powerful word as *agonistes* or "wrestling with." To wrestle with ideas is a powerful metaphor for how to cope with the challenges of a post-modern world.

The very idea of effort is the very essence of the word for an ancient Greek athlete. The Olympic games in Greek are known as *agones*. And competitions were not limited to the physical contests. The great tragedies of Sophocles, Aeschylus, and Euripides were all products of dramatic festivals described as *agones*.

Aeschylus' above quote was a favorite of Robert F. Kennedy, who was said to have found both pain and solace in immersing himself in these words. Suffering is the beginning of wisdom.

For the Greeks to suffer and struggle were intertwined with the contest but, more importantly, linked to the inherent desire to excel. They willingly embraced pain and competed to be the best version of themselves.

> *"So be strict with yourself, like a good athlete of God."*
>
> ~St. Ignatius of Antioch.

Inline with agon and struggle is a closely linked concept of *askesis*, which may be translated into practice, training, exercise, or, more specifically, *athletic discipline*. Although in modern parlance, asceticism is usually only associated with those in the spiritual disciplines, it has a much broader application.

Professor David Fagerberg describes asceticism as the exercise, the effort, the labor expended to attain a goal. He goes on to say, "The ascetic has patience because it is the opposite of despondency, which so often results from a desire for instant gratification."

Jim Rohn, the famous motivational speaker who mentored Tony Robbins, liked to say, "There is the pain of discipline and the pain of regret." Research has shown that *super-agers*, those who live very long lives, succeed partly because they can push past pain.

Embrace the struggle of life *agon* and wrestle with the pain of discipline through practice and training to compete as an athlete of life.

Dr. Sam Pappas is a board-certified physician in Internal Medicine who uniquely combines the best of traditional and integrative medicine to optimize patient care. He completed medical school at Pennsylvania State College of Medicine and his residency training, including a year as Chief Resident, at Case Western Reserve University/University Hospital in Cleveland, Ohio. He brings over 20 years of experience and has practiced in a variety of diverse positions in both academic health centers and private practice in roles as a clinician, educator, and administrator. He has been selected as a top doctor in the Washingtonian Magazine, Northern Virginia Magazine, Washington Consumers Checkbook and has been called *The Dr. Oz of Arlington* by MONA- The Mothers of Northern Arlington. He is a member of the Institute of Functional Medicine (IFM), the American Academy of Anti-Aging Medicine (A4M), and the Metabolic Medical Institute (MMI), transformative health care organizations that seek to shift the paradigm from organ-based diseases to functional dynamic systems that stress the importance of root causes. He now runs his own unique practice, Pappas Health, that incorporates innovative services encompassing both a high tech and high touch approach while maintaining the best of holistic and traditional medicine in a collaborative environment. He is a native of New Jersey, fluent in Greek, and is married with three children. You can find more information at www.pappashealth.com.

CHAPTER 14

DISCOVERING THE WONDER WOMAN IN YOU

FINDING YOUR SUPERPOWER THROUGH PASSION, PURPOSE, AND FEARLESSNESS

Pamela Bolado

MY STORY

Fearlessness—that elusive blend of self-acceptance, confidence, and curiosity—is the defining quality of those who find their superpower.

Looming over the rocky horizon and endless valleys of the Himalayas, I could begin to see glaciers and Mount Everest's summit. As the world tallest and famous mountain approached me, I was surprised at how imperfect it was in comparison to its counterparts. It was spectacular in its own way, rough around the edges, but still a beauty to behold. Could this be a representation of me? Did I find myself in the reflection of Everest? This imperfect structure that the outside world viewed as perfect.

One of the women who joined me on this trek shared how perfect she thought I was from seeing me on social media. We had never met prior to this adventure. It made my eyebrows raise and almost feel sad, really. "I am far from perfect," I told her. By the end of the 18 days, she had seen me cry, vent, and un-showered for longer than one would like. The perception of perfectionism is what I dislike most about social media. We are *not* perfect, but perfectly imperfect.

Let me first share that I understand we all have a story. It took me a long time to believe in myself and believe my story is important and that it can inspire others to be better tomorrow than they are today. So is yours! What will you do with your passion? How can you shift your mindset to find your purpose? What does being fearless mean to you? Do we all have a superpower? So many questions. I have asked myself these questions over the years and finally discovered the answers. I want to help you discover your own answers to be the wonder woman that you are.

EVEREST

I could see the strings of flags blowing in the wind from a distance—the finish line. I did it! My little legs made it to Everest Base Camp. Challenge complete and goal attained! I think it has become an addiction over the years. What challenges can I set for myself? What do I have to do to achieve them?

This isn't a "how-to" chapter on being fearless. It's part of my story and experiences. I hope it gives you the tools to help you prepare mentally, physically, and spiritually to face your fearlessness straight on. Where did I find my passion and purpose, my unrelenting superpower? My guts and glory? My never-ending determination and resiliency?

I recently had the opportunity to find those answers. I found them standing in the middle of the Himalayas. I decided at the age of 43 that I was going to climb to Mt. Everest Base Camp. Why? Because I knew that I could. I knew it would be no different than the mountains I've climbed throughout my life. This time I really had to push my body both mentally and physically. I set out on a journey to take one step at a time to the tallest mountain in the world. Mt. Everest was looming in the great distance. I could taste my end goal, but it was still 88,000 steps ahead of me.

When I set out on the rocky path and quite literally dodged yak poo, it was a test of my mental health and would enable me to venture into new zones and dreams I could never have imagined. With every short step, I moved towards my goal of 17,600ft. *Could my little five-foot-one legs make it?*

Would I acclimate well and be able to handle the hazards of being at altitude? This was going to test my mental and physical fortitude like nothing I'd ever done before.

I don't use the word 'hate' very often. However, let me tell you how much I hate the cold and camping. I have never really liked climbing. This was going to be the challenge of my life.

We began the journey by visiting villages to meet and empower young Nepali girls. As the newly appointed United States of America's Mrs. Gulf Breeze, Florida, I brought tiaras and made handprinted sashes with empowering messages on them to pass to the little girls. I honored each girl as the queen she is and told them, "You can be anything you set your heart to be!"

The next day, we began our seven-day trek to Everest Base Camp through the pouring rain. Our first place of rest was a town called, Namshe. It had not rained like it did that day for the past nine years. So, of course, it had to occur on my first day! All I can tell you is that I had time to reflect on my life, mission, purpose, my true passion, and my superpower. Did I have to travel to Nepal to push my body's limits to find it? Probably not; however, it gave me the permission to breathe and think about self-care. I needed to find myself. I can't think of a time in my life that I had 18 days to focus only on myself. I can't think of even a few consecutive days. Despite being challenged by altitude, nourishments, and the elements, I found my purpose in those mountains.

When I finally made it to Everest Base Camp, the feeling of victory filled my eyes, the cold air in my lungs, and I felt complete. *I can do anything!* I held my Mission Wonder Women flag high and proud and then popped my mini bottle of prosecco to celebrate. Only one sip, though—I still have to trek back down the treacherous mountain.

YOUNG PAM

As I stare at myself in the mirror: I tell my childhood self, "Hi sweet girl, you will grow up to be strong, beautiful, and fearless. Wipe away those tears; ignore those kids on the playground. You are much stronger than you think. You will see!"

I was born in Canada with a cleft lip and grew up looking in the mirror wondering, *why me?* I didn't know anyone else who looked like me. After many years of low self-esteem, I finally began to love myself and embrace my scar. I took my fear and pain and transformed that into my twenty-year career helping other women to feel beautiful about themselves. I became an international award-winning medical esthetician at the age of nineteen and worked all over the world.

How can I share my entire life in one chapter? I'll break it down, so you better understand who I am—an open book. I've been broken and put back together and made into a stronger version of myself over the years. I feel blessed every day to have lived and experienced cultures around the globe. And to be honest, I wouldn't take back any of the hardships I've encountered as it's thickened my skin. I'm a resilient achiever! I suffered from low self-esteem and acceptance. Sometimes I asked myself, "Were you my friend because you felt sorry for me? You don't have to say I'm pretty to make me feel better." I had trust issues as a young girl, seeking the truth, not knowing what to believe.

Although I was good at hiding my emotions and insecurities, it made me seek perfectionism, constantly trying to prove myself to be accepted. This can be quite exhausting. Maybe this was my hidden superpower. Maybe I was meant to be born different to better understand my purpose later in my life. Maybe the tears, feelings of unworthiness, and frustration were all there to build my shell.

Some of my notable achievements were junior high school student council Vice President and President, being the first female amateur boxer from New Brunswick, Canada, being a dancer, and being an Air Cadet. I tried it all, trying to find who I was.

MY NIGHT IN SHINING ARMOR

I met my first husband at the age of 19; he was 11 years my senior. We met in Canada, then moved to London, where we eloped at a mosque. He was Muslim; I was Christian. That meant nothing to me; only our love mattered. At 21, we moved to Kuwait, his homeland, just before 9/11.

I resided in Kuwait during Operation Iraqi Freedom in 2003; my first-born son was one year old at the time. I was stubborn and didn't listen to pleas for foreigners to leave the country amid threats of chemical weapons from Saddam Hussein. I stayed and built a makeshift shelter in my home where we would seek refuge during war sirens of missile threats.

This was certainly a scary time; however, it was the beginning of major shifts in my life. The personal shifts often seemed much scarier than the chemical threats. I nonchalantly recall these times in my life. They were pinnacle moments in hardening my shell. My self-doubt and self-esteem issues seemed to begin to fade, and a new, more mature me was emerging.

My first marriage crumbled; I restarted my life back in Canada, where I took night classes in entrepreneurship. Then I started a company, built a brick n' mortar in a sweet little copper-colored Victorian house. Shortly after, I turned around and closed it a year and a half later to move back across the world with only a few suitcases and a baby on my hip. There's a whole story in between those sentences.

I'm now a single mother living alone in the heart of Kuwait. I went back to my previous job in the hospital managing the Medical Esthetics Department. At this point in my life, I feel like a failure. How will I move on? Then, I meet this incredible man who has helped me forget the sadness and feelings of failure. A U.S. Air Force pilot. At first, I doubted marrying into the military. Thinking it wouldn't be a wise decision. I put that worry aside and moved to the U.S. in 2016 when we decided to take the leap of faith. His deployment to Kuwait and my bravery to go back across the pond by myself was our destiny. I have owned and honored the role of military wife and now use it to support my sisters both in the military and worldwide.

MENTAL FORTITUDE

How do you develop the mental fortitude to believe in yourself and your purpose? One key change I've committed to making over the years is to become fearless in my own journey. The main trigger points of my anxieties begin with that first thought of fear. It becomes monstrous in my mind, and before I know it, I'm having a panic attack and then completely unproductive. The question I found myself asking is, "What is my superpower?"

My life motto! BE BETTER TOMORROW THAN YOU WERE TODAY!

I decided to give up my award-winning, international career and follow what I'm most passionate about: Women! I support women any way I can. When I moved back to Canada from the Middle East in 2010, I embarked on a journey of entrepreneurship. Living alone with two young boys, I took any course I could find and sought out any free resource to help me start my business. It was tough. I was navigating the unknown.

Through years of trying, doing, failing, and trying again, I discovered how sweet the feeling of helping another woman overcome an obstacle made me feel. It was exhilarating and filled my heart more than the dollars that filled my pockets from my successful career.

Celebrate the victories. Own your failures. Keep going.

Winning is when you don't give up. Fearlessness is a form of success. Success in life begins with achieving your goals, whatever they may be. Maybe you want to write a book, become a lawyer, or learn how to garden. Each of these goals has barriers and challenges to overcome. Pushing through those barriers, persevering, growing personally, and helping others will help you achieve ultimate success and fearlessness. I've been supporting women for as long as I can remember, believing we are the most resilient beings alive. I'm resilient, but I'm no different than you!

I'm blessed to have friends from all walks of life, from royalty to career-driven women to mompreneurs to stay-at-home super mamas. I can assure you we are all the same, just in different ways. Our visions may be different, but the goal is the same. It always comes down to your passion, purpose, and fearlessness. I live my days always wondering, *what if? What if I could be better tomorrow? What challenge can I create in my space to fulfill my need for betterment? Will I inspire my sisters to also achieve their greatness?* We live only one time. Do you want to look back wishing you had done that one thing as the years go by?

How can I inspire you to go outside of your comfort zones, push your limits, believe in yourself, and help you find your superpower? When you realize each opportunity laid before you is a privilege and you're not entitled, gratitude fills your soul. Saying goodbye to my career and pursuing my passion for supporting women from all walks of life gave me the deepest joy. It's also very important to note that it takes support, love, and understanding from those around you. Without unconditional support, it can be difficult to tap into your deepest joy.

My story is still being written, and I don't plan on slowing down anytime soon. I have new goals to attain and women to empower!

THE TOOL

FIND YOUR SUPERPOWER

PASSION

A feeling of intense enthusiasm towards or compelling desire for something. Enthusiastic enjoyment of an interest or activity.

PURPOSE

When you do something with purpose, you do it with determination. When your activities have a purpose, you have an aim or intention in mind.

FEARLESS

To be bold or brave. The blend of self-acceptance, confidence, and curiosity—is the defining quality of those who find their superpower.

My road is ever-winding, and it has taken me 43 years not to get lost. Finding your mountain, your summit, your Everest is about looking inward and finding you first. To help you do that, grab a notepad and answer these questions:

What ultimately makes you happy?

If you had all the time and money in the world, what would you do with it?

Stop, close your eyes, and really look inward.

To determine your superpower, understand that to find clarity about your end mission, you must find your strengths, tackle your self-awareness, and understand who you really are and what you excel at. If you think about it, superheroes all have similar goals, but their abilities are polar opposite. Sometimes, we look at what others are doing and use that to measure our success, but we should really be looking at our own strengths to determine success.

Finding your superpower and determining your superior strength can help you understand where you can be the most successful in both your personal and professional life.

When are you feeling fearless?

Think about the times you've felt the most confident. Think of a time when you felt the most comfortable going outside your comfort zone and truly testing your abilities.

Finding that comfort level will cast a light on your strength in that area. Most of the time, the things that you truly enjoy are the things you're good at.

I often envision myself achieving my end goal, imagining what that would look like and feel like. It gives me a sense of excitement and anticipation toward reaching my achievement.

Getting clarity about your strengths and discovering your superpower will make all the difference in your career and life journey. We all have individual strengths, and we're all capable of achieving our goals at our own pace and in our unique way.

What do you do that amazes others?

Are we born with superpowers, or can we earn them through the experiences and strengths we build over the years? We can one hundred percent earn them, and they can be fueled through our passions. Superpowers are found between your passion, purpose, and strengths. We all have one; some of us have several. But let's focus on that one that makes us stand out, like Wonder Woman and Superman. You know you have passion when something not only makes you happy but motivates you and makes you want to work harder for it.

I know I've found my passion when time melts away, and I find myself completely enthralled with my end goal. I've thought about the times I've been the most successful and achieved my goals, such as competing in my first body-building competition at the age of 41 and walking away with nine medals around my neck, several plaques, and a tiara. There was also launching my magazine in under a month, starting my nonprofit, and my most recent accomplishment, reaching Mt. Everest Base Camp. All of them started with an exciting idea that transformed into a reality. But how did I reach my end goals? What was my driving factor to fearlessness and finding my superpower?

SELF-CARE

Another key factor in fueling your superpower is the importance of self-care which means taking care of yourself to be healthy, well, and maintain the energy to fuel your passion, purpose, and strengths. You cannot get to your destination running on low fuel.

Here are a few important and simple self-care examples to practice every day:

- Maintaining a regular sleep routine

- Eating healthy

- Spending time in Nature

- Doing a hobby you enjoy (this could be your passion and purpose)

- Expressing your gratitude

- Self-care can look different for everyone, but to classify as self-care, the action should promote health and happiness for you.

Passion, purpose, fearlessness (and a little self-care): Find your superpowers and change the world!

Pamela recently completed her trek to Mt. Everest BC (17,600ft) and the summit of Kalamathar (elevation of 18,519ft) to raise funds and awareness for mental health and wellness.

Pamela is an ambitious entrepreneur. Born in Canada, mother of three, and a military spouse.

While living abroad for a total of 13 years, she's founded several small businesses and is an avid volunteer for not-for-profit organizations.

Born with a cleft lip, she continues to be a committed advocate for Smile Train and currently sits on the 2021 Smile Train Cleft Advisory Council.

Pamela is also passionate about assisting organizations that work to end human trafficking, building a future for girls and women, mental health, and supporting our women of the military/ first responders.

Pamela is excited to amplify her passion for philanthropy by creating a global community

ready to tackle the challenges of today and tomorrow and make a better world for everyone. In December 2020, she formed the organization Women Who Do Wonders International and her nonprofit, Mission Wonder Women Foundation, where she advocates for women and children.

Ultimately, Pamela would like to inspire others to pay it forward in their communities and businesses.

If not you, then who? If not now, then when?

I invite you to become part of my community of Women Who Do Wonders. If there's one thing I know, it's that when women pool know-how, heart-driven meaningful work, and connections, we are unstoppable!

You can find more tools and resources at www.womenwhodowonders.org/wellness

Follow Pamela and join the community at Women Who Do Wonders

IG @Pamela_Bolado @WomenWhoDoWonders

Clubhouse & LinkedIn @PamelaBolado

Email- pamela@womenwhodowonders.com

Join the community at www.womenwhodowonders.org

CHAPTER 15

YOU'VE GOT THIS!

HEALING THROUGH STRETCH AND SELF-MASSAGE

Rorrie Sisk, LMT

MY STORY

I fell in a snowbank.

Let me correct that. I fell down three flights of stairs into a snowbank.

It was the winter of 2007 in Mid-Hudson Valley, New York. I delivered my son a few months earlier, in December, by way of C-section. I lived in an apartment on the top floor of a three-story exterior walk-up and just got the baby and my six-year-old daughter inside. I had to go back down to get groceries out of the car.

The stairs were salted that morning; however, they were iced over again in some places when we got home that evening. As I was getting the kids into the apartment and thought, *I should throw some ice melt out before I go back down* again. Somehow I must have forgotten in a few minutes I was back inside because I definitely did not throw ice melt out. I blame the "new mom brain." It's a thing.

I don't think I even managed to get down the first step. I remember reaching for the banister as my feet, stairs, and ice all worked together in betrayal of my balance. It happened in slow motion, and yet it was over in a matter of seconds. I remember hitting my head on one of the railing posts. Mostly, I was impressed I managed to pretty much fall on my butt the whole way down until I was deposited into the snowbank at the bottom, next to my parked car.

I looked up at the clear winter sky full of stars and tried to decide if I was hurt or not.

"What the hell was that?" my downstairs neighbor yelled.

She heard a commotion and was now standing on the sidewalk outside our building, looking around. She didn't see me at first.

"Um. It was me," I said weakly. "I fell down the stairs."

She squinted toward where she heard my voice.

"Oh my God! Are you in the snowbank!?"

"Yes. I believe I'm in the snowbank," I answered.

"Are you okay?" she asked.

"I'm in a fucking snowbank," I said as I started laughing. "And I think my boobs are leaking."

We both burst into uncontrollable laughter as she helped me out of the snow and onto my feet. It was freezing. That made the leaking breastmilk incredibly uncomfortable. After assuring her I was fine, I grabbed the bag of groceries and headed back upstairs, carefully.

When I got up the next morning, I had a bruise that extended from my lower back down my left leg to the back of my knee. It was a few gruesome shades of deep blue and green and nearly black in some areas. Oddly, I wasn't in pain. Maybe a little stiff, but not in pain. Unfortunately, that was temporary.

About two weeks later, as I got out of bed, I started to stand up straight and felt a jolt of pain in my lower back. I could not get myself to stand up straight without feeling that jolt. It felt like a little bit of electricity zapped me every time I tried to straighten up. I thought maybe I slept wrong and took an Ibuprofen, thinking it would work itself out during the day.

But it didn't, for weeks. Finally, I decided I should probably see a doctor to figure out what the heck was going on with me. As it turned out, I had several herniated discs, likely due to my tumble into the snowbank. At the time, it was recommended I have surgery. I declined and instead opted for injections to ease the pain. The injections helped, but the pain was always there on some level. And then one of my doctors recommended massages.

I never really thought of massage as a modality that could be therapeutic for injury. My previous experience with massage was that it was a relaxing and somewhat luxurious experience. I went to the massage therapist the doctor recommended and was absolutely blown away by the difference a few sessions made. But it was expensive. And my insurance didn't cover it. I continued to go as often as I could afford and noticed the difference when I couldn't go regularly.

A few years passed, and we relocated to Northern Virginia. I decided to change careers but couldn't think of what else I might want to do with my life. I worked as a substance abuse counselor for over a decade and knew I wanted to continue to work in a profession where I was helping people but didn't know what that would look like. I scrolled through different job listings, trying to see if anything leapt out at me. I noticed that I kept seeing an ad for a massage school and thought, I would love to do that, to help people through massage. *So I enrolled.*

It turned out massage school was just the entry point for my journey in learning about healing the body through touch. I've taken many different trainings on various types of bodywork, all of which contribute to the tools I use in creating an individualized treatment for my clients. I realized that many of my clients found themselves in the same situation I was in, feeling the benefits of massage but unable to afford to come as often as they needed to. This got me thinking about how I could pass along tools to my clients that they could use on themselves.

And then it hit me. *We all have the tools.* All I needed to do was to remind my clients of things they already knew!

THE TOOL

SELF-MASSAGE AND STRETCH

Massage and stretch are both effective ways to help relax your muscles, release tension, and lessen stress and anxiety. When you cannot have bodywork done, you can still utilize massage and stretching techniques to help your body feel better. Self-massage and stretching have also been known to prolong the benefits from professional massage and help to provide relief in between sessions. The best part is that you already know how to do it! No, really! You do!

Think for a moment about the last time you hit your shin on something. What did you do? Most people instinctively will apply pressure or rub the area to soothe it. What areas do you touch when you have a headache? What about when your neck hurts? How are you moving to alleviate that hurt? When you move from a position you've been in for a while, do you stretch your arms and legs? I'll bet you do.

Each of us has these instincts on how to care for our bodies when they are achy or hurting. It's a matter of listening to those instincts in relation to what you're feeling in your body. That is the tool: you, your instincts, and your touch.

Here's how to use it:

LISTENING:

The first step is to listen to your body. Close your eyes if you can, and listen to what your body is telling you. Where in your body is your attention being drawn? Take note of areas that you feel are stiff, achy, or tense.

POSITIONING:

Get into a position that allows you the most movement and comfort with the space you have. If you're in a tight space like a plane, this may be very limited, and if you have a lot of room, feel free to spread out. You can work with just about any space. When you've found a good position, take a few slow breaths and think again about the areas of your body calling out to you.

MOVEMENT:

The key to feeling better using bodywork is movement. This can be the movement of your hands over parts of your body (massage), and it can also mean moving your body in different directions (stretch). Self-massage techniques can be kneading, rubbing, and even light tapping. Self-stretching methods involve moving your body in ways that will lengthen tissue where you feel tight or restricted.

Whether you are starting with self-massage or stretching, the only rule is to listen to your body. Use a gentle touch to begin and gradually increase pressure or deepen the stretch as your body allows. Take note of what feels good as well as what doesn't. Do more of the good.

EXAMPLE:

Let's imagine you are on a plane, and your neck and lower back are bothering you. To massage, you could start with your fingertips at the top of your neck and move them in small gentle circular motions toward your collar bones or shoulders. To stretch, you may move your head from side to side, gently exploring what movements feel good to you and seem to release some of the tension you're feeling. You could also raise and lower your shoulders or roll them back. All of these motions can be made right in your seat.

Be mindful of what your body is telling you. If your pain is severe, you have an open wound, suspect a fracture, or are experiencing numbness or tingling, be sure to seek medical help. Self-massage and stretch are beautiful ways to reduce aches and pains, release tension, and reduce anxiety and stress; however, they are not replacements for medical care.

I invite you to tune into your body and explore what movements of massage and stretch feel good to you. Listen to your body. Use your tools. You've got this!

Rorrie Sisk is a person who is curious and compassionate about the world around her and the people in it. This curiosity and compassion drive her work as a Licensed Massage Therapist, Licensed Esthetician, reiki practitioner, and owner at Great Lengths LLC in Falls Church, Virginia. Rorrie is originally from the Mid-Hudson Valley in New York, where she worked as a substance abuse counselor specializing in treatment with adolescents for over a decade. After relocating to Northern Virginia, Rorrie shifted her passion for healing and care to bodywork and eventually esthetics and reiki. No matter the service, Rorrie brings her unique skill set to customize services tailored to the needs of each individual. Rorrie's professional associations include the American Massage Therapy Association (AMTA), the Associated Bodywork & Massage Professionals (ABMP), and Associated Skin Care Professionals (ASCP).

Rorrie is a mother of two children who she identifies as being the greatest joys of her life. She loves spending time with friends and family, singing karaoke, and exploring different cuisines.

You can explore more of Rorrie's craft on Instagram at @GreatLengthsDC or by checking out her website at www.GreatLengthsDC.com.

CHAPTER 16

FROM THE BURDEN OF RESPONSIBILITY TO FREEDOM

LETTING GO OF WHAT WASN'T YOURS TO BEGIN WITH

Micole Noble

MY STORY

I entered the world in darkness through a C-section that nearly killed my mother.

The ever-present reminder being those first photos in which I could have easily been mistaken for little more than a loaf of bread, swaddled tightly next to my mother's jaundiced arm.

"I almost died having you."

It was a refrain I heard often.

Several years earlier, my parents lost my infant brother, waking to find him no longer breathing in his crib—what today would be known as, *SIDS*, or Sudden Infant Death Syndrome.

My parents, of course, were devastated by the loss. And unable to cope themselves, let alone help each other, they parted ways.

As it turned out, however, their story wasn't over, and just a couple years later, I was born.

I exist because my brother died.

I remember knowing that before I could walk. I was my parents' last *Lifetime-movie-worthy* chance at happiness together, the replacement for the happiness they lost in my hand-me-down crib. It was something I felt from my chubby fingers all the way down to my chubby toes.

I was responsible for all of it, though if truth be told, I didn't quite understand what *"it"* was. But at two years old, I was definitely responsible nonetheless.

And it was around then that my parents' filed for their second (and last) divorce.

"I almost died having you," my mother reminded my four-year-old self.

I wasn't tall enough to reach my favorite snack at the back of the kitchen counter, even on tippy toes, or imagine what might await me in kindergarten a year or two from then, but I was certain I was responsible for my mom's *almost death.*

That I knew for sure.

My fault. My fault. My fault.

I was *definitely* responsible.

A couple of years after my parents' second divorce, my mom married the man who would become my dad, *Pops*. Pops was my hero —the kindest man I'd ever met, with the biggest blue eyes I'd ever seen. He raised me with the love and understanding I'd been hoping for. I felt seen. *This*, I felt, *was what home felt like.*

After Mom married Pops, I spent holidays and summers jetting off to faraway places to visit my father, who often met me at the airport with women on his arm I'd never met before. Women with curled hair and pretty lipstick who didn't seem to like me very much.

Sit-downs with my father during these occasions always seemed to make their way to discussions of child support payments and the expenses of living in Southern California.

And I walked away knowing without a doubt:

I was responsible for the expenses of living where we did.

I was the reason my mom was asking for more child support.

My mom's third divorce came with hardly a warning, but it wasn't like she regularly consulted with me.

She wasn't yet 40 years old when she told me, "Stay in school and don't get knocked up when you're 15, like I did."

As it turned out, I didn't.

Always curious, I excelled in school and lived for reading books and practicing my handwriting. Mom didn't finish the ninth grade, so she hardly encouraged me to work on my college admissions essays.

There wasn't money for "that" anyway.

"Get a job and you'll be fine," she said.

Stay in school, get a job, don't get knocked up.

I would be responsible.

I ended up being one of those stories you hear about when someone finds their soulmate in high school at 15, and had it stick. And Todd and I moved in together five years later.

Not long after, Todd was in a horrific car accident, one from which he "walked away," but one from which his best friend didn't. The fallout was beyond traumatic. And we were incredibly young. It was one of those situations that could have ended everything. But it somehow cemented our relationship and deepened my commitment. I could see the life we'd have together.

After our fairy-tale, puffy-white-dress wedding, we lived the American dream—two incomes, two kids, two dogs and a beautiful home in San Diego, short-lived though the dream was.

My long commute coupled with kids in daycare for too many hours and a recruiting job that left me feeling "meh," I was perpetually short on time, not (ever) present and 100% unfulfilled.

Unbeknownst to me, the entire journey to this point had teed me up for my very unplanned—though very welcome—spiritual journey.

Never one to go into anything half in or half out, I went from zero awareness to self-help junkie seemingly overnight. I didn't want one more thing to add to my to-do list or one more piece of information.

I wanted transformation.

And I was desperately looking for it anywhere I thought it might be lurking.

I returned to college to finish my degree, and followed a friend to my first yoga retreat, where admittedly, I found love for only the second time in my life.

I took my turn as a life coach and got certified (a logical jump from recruiting to coaching) I thought.

I found that while I was easily manifesting the things I outwardly wanted most, I was still feeling mentally exhausted and over-obligated.

When the effects of the COVID-19 pandemic hit the U.S. in early 2020, the world seemed to awaken to the idea we've all heard and read in movies, songs and pieces of great literature for nearly our entire lives—"Life is so uncertain."

Before the global shutdown, I myself had secretly been asking for this ride called life to come to a complete stop.

After years of seeking, I had found.

Only to want to find again.

There had to be more.

During this time, my eldest son did what I had only silently dreamed of for many years—selling everything and buying a one-way ticket to Maui. The FOMO was real, as was my feeling that I had to GTFO.

I had spent years coaching my clients to choose the lives they were dreaming of.

When I realized I wasn't walking the talk.

But then again, I was a mom, wife, yoga and meditation teacher, and coach and responsible for *so many other things* in my day to day life, from grocery aficionado to counselor and friend.

I was responsible.

So was I really as *free* as I told my clients and students *they* were?

As free as I *pretended* to be?

And when I got down to the crux of it, the answer was pretty simple.

I had the option to choose whatever I wanted.

The belief that I alone was responsible for everyone (and everything) in my life was so ingrained, I was actually creating my entire waking experience around shouldering the weight of it all.

So I began to unravel my thoughts and beliefs around the belief:

I am responsible.

I asked questions, and lots of them:

- To whom am I responsible?
- And for what specifically?
- Better yet, why?
- Are the things I feel responsibility for even mine to own?
- Does anyone I feel responsible for realize I took that on?
- Or am I the only participant in a one-sided game of tag?
- Am I giving my power away?
- And if so, why would I do that willingly?
- Am I getting something out of feeling responsible for others?
- Does it make me feel needed?
- Did I take on someone else's issues, hurts, or problems as my own?
- And if so, why?

And the one that really got me thinking:

- If I didn't take on responsibility that wasn't mine to take on in the first place, what could I do with all that extra time and *freedom* instead?

Day by day, little by little, I asked myself these questions, unwound the old tangled messes of patterns, examined the pieces, and worked to let go of the ones keeping me stuck in an outdated sense of "owing."

I sat in silence. I meditated. I did yoga. I walked on the beach. I surrendered.

And I created a new belief:

I am FREE right now.

And something started to shift.

Because it was only by creating this new belief that I could create a new experience—one of living consciously at the level of spirit. One where I already had all the knowledge, support and abundance I needed. Where life could become simple, with less distractions, more connection and WAY less hangups, feelings of guilt, and old, outdated responsibilities I took on (that weren't mine to hold in the first place).

I practiced feeling what it meant to actually be free from all that in both my body and mind. And by doing that, I naturally drew more of that experience of freedom I was looking for, into my inner being.

THE TOOL

So what does it look like to Be, Do and Have when you are happy, present, peaceful, and unattached to the responsibility you assumed on your shoulders?

You:

- Cultivate a daily meditation and/or yoga practice

- Practice present-moment awareness, noticing those little experiences happening all around you **all the time** *(hello there, Mr. Butterfly on my car)*

- Become immune to what others think, because "What they think of you is none of your business." I borrowed that one from Deepak

- Don't take on what isn't yours to take on in the first place (and give other people their own power back to handle **their own** responsibilities)

- Notice when you become anxious and stop in the moment to figure out what it was that triggered you

- Pay less attention to social media and television

- Put your phone away as much as possible

In short, this exercise taught me how many distractions were pulling me out of the present. They were causing me to live in fear of the future, instead of creating the life I wanted now in the present.

The past had been weighing me down for far too long.

Fast forward just over a year, and I now have a profitable business, happier relationships with others, and the ability to travel to my sacred space in Maui every quarter and stay for a month! Taking time to retreat has been an important piece of my journey and I became keenly aware of this need to go inward and be in solitude regularly during the time the world shut down.

Now it's time to do some spring cleaning (or fall as the case may be here in the states). It's your turn to shake off those layers of self-imposed responsibility like a pair of drapes that haven't been cleaned in decades (am I right?).

BE-DO-HAVE

If your life was ideal, what would it look like?

Now, write your answers to these questions down below. And I encourage you to write this in present tense, like it's already here, *because it can be!*

What does this look like for you? Really take a moment to feel into each one.

When my life is ideal, I AM:

Being:

Doing:

Having:

Mostly we've been taught to think about what we want to **have** (car, house, career), so that we can **do** (all the things), and *then* we will **be** (happy, successful, or fill-in-the blank) when it actually works the other way around.

When we are being our ideals *right now*, we begin to draw that energy of what we want to create to us. In fact, it's a universal law. That energy just can't help but flow to us freely.

Life becomes simple, smooth, and effortless. Through a consistent meditation practice and clear intentions, our experience of life expands on our own terms, because we know what's ours to take on, and more importantly, what's not.

And with the newfound awareness we'll come to, the possibilities are truly endless.

Here are a couple of tips you can try to help untangle yourself from those old habits and patterns. And just a note—remember to be patient with yourself. This is not easy stuff, but it will make your daily life so much easier once you start reclaiming your inner freedom.

1. Set your intention for a life free from worry, responsibilities and struggle that aren't yours, and then practice present moment awareness. Detach from the outcome or what you think your life should look like. Trust that the Universe has something even better in store for you than you ever could have imagined for yourself.

2. Getting what we want becomes a natural byproduct of who we are being, and taking inspired actions. Hiring a coach or mentor to guide you can be helpful to manage old thought patterns and let go of limiting beliefs.

FEEL into the *experience* you want to have.

Can you feel that way now?

Rehearse it.

Conjure it up.

It's *your* creation.

And it's your responsibility to live the life you were meant to live.

All that other stuff you've picked up along the way that wasn't yours to begin with?

Just shake it off.

Micole is passionate about guiding others to their best life. Her belief is in a consciousness-based approach to teaching and coaching and she is a Certified Chopra Master Educator, Chopra Faculty member, and Chopra Mentor Coach. Teaching the *Seven Spiritual Laws of Yoga* is a specialty of hers, and she is obsessed with Yoga philosophy and history. This along with her corporate experience makes sharing the sister sciences of Yoga and Meditation to reduce stress in the workplace a calling of hers as well.

Micole guides her clients back to themselves by facilitating presence, peace, and by listening with intention for what they are committed to. The experience is one of lightness, purpose, and an overall expansion of Self.

Working with Micole is described as heart-centered, simple, and transformational guidance that is infused with wisdom, humor, and empathy.

Encouraging others to follow their dreams and desires by taking a leap to become an entrepreneur, feeling the fear about something and deciding to do it anyway, and having the courage to tell the truth about what they really want are some of the ways Micole helps to shift others toward their unique gift or talent.

Micole is a logophile and has a keen appreciation and fascination for how humans use language to create both our inner and outer worlds. She actually *is* the change she wants to see in the world.

Micole holds a BS degree in Communication with a mass media focus from California State University, San Marcos, and has two life coaching certifications, in addition to being a 2019 graduate of lululemon's 200-hour Yoga & Leadership program, mind.ful.on.

She lives with her husband and two dogs in Carlsbad, CA and has two grown boys.

Find and follow Micole here:

www.MicoleNoble.com

Instagram: @micolenoble

Facebook: https://www.facebook.com/micolenoble

Linked In: https://www.linkedin.com/in/micolenoble

https://heal.me/micole-noble-life-coach

CHAPTER 17

PLAY

THE MISSING INGREDIENT IN SELF-CARE

Alison Qualter, CPC, ELI-MP

*"We don't stop playing because we grow old,
we grow old because we stop playing."*

~George Bernard Shaw

MY STORY

Guilt was an unwanted friend that seemed to hang around me whenever I made decisions as a working mother, especially when those decisions had anything to do with choosing myself.

I remember the very moment I kicked her out the door.

When I was a little girl, I always dreamed of being a mother. I had other dreams, too, usually related to a future business I would start—maybe a coffee shop, or a school, or a bookstore that might also sell flowers.

By the time I turned 40, I was a proud mother of three loving, hilarious children, and I was a co-founder of Apple Seeds: an all-in-one children's play space with three New York City locations, two international locations, and a national franchise for our kids' music program, Songs for Seeds. I dove deeply into both roles: mother and business owner. I worked nearly seven days a week at hours that I chose, and this flexibility allowed me to volunteer at my children's schools and be as present as possible. The more I did for my kids and my work, the more accomplished I felt. But over time, I realized something was missing. I felt a space in my heart. It was a kind of longing, despite how full my life seemed.

It felt bizarre and even entitled to think I could want more than what I already had, but as time passed, I began to see I'd let an important part of myself hibernate far too long. *I had forgotten how to have fun.* I didn't yet realize that no matter how many responsibilities I had or how much older I got, or even how trauma from my past might weigh me down, I was still allowed to play and do things just for me.

The inner athlete in me was longing to come out. I used to be a gymnast who played soccer and a swimmer who loved to rock climb—the more challenging the sport, the better. I was an avid traveler and looked for opportunities to go for a run in any new town or country I'd visit. I began to realize that by diving into work and motherhood, I locked in these parts of myself for far too long.

I found the key accidentally when I heard about a week-long yoga challenge in New York City and, to my surprise, spontaneously signed up. It meant I had to take a week off from work and family to do 15 yoga classes in five days. Insert guilt here. What if my son potty trained while I was in savasana, relaxing on the mat? How could I dare miss my daughter's cello concert or my other daughter's Spanish presentation? What if my partners at work needed me? How could I be so selfish?

In that very first class, I remember I couldn't quite sink into a state of Zen. My body was on the mat, but my mind was somewhere else, heavy with guilt. But, as the week wore on, I noticed I began to let go and finally relax and enjoy being in the flow of this passion of mine.

When I got home from that final yoga class, I was hesitant to walk in the door, worried that my kids might not be fed, dressed, or worse—what if they were angry with me for being absent for five full days? Instead of that reaction, I vividly remember how my seven-year-old twin girls ran and hugged me when I walked into our apartment. They just kept saying how happy I seemed and asked when I was going to do yoga again.

And it was right there that I had my lightbulb moment. What had I been doing slaving away at all of the tasks in front of me, never prioritizing what might be good—or fun—for me? Work defined so much of my purpose in life, and being a parent was my everything. I thought taking time for myself would disappoint my kids. But what did my kids want most of all? They wanted my happiness. My energy affected their energy, as well as everyone else around me. I saw how taking time to play and do what I love, for no specific result other than joy, had a broader impact.

That is how my kids gave me the permission I needed to play a little bit more and squeeze the most out of my one life.

I thought of the options. *Maybe I could restart tennis? Or perhaps I could get back to the piano I learned as a child? Or dive into a new language, maybe French? Or try something totally new, like, knitting? No way. I can't sit still long enough.*

I decided to come up with some sort of athletic-challenge-meets-travel-adventure every year. I shifted my once guilt-ridden, overwhelmed, and busy mindset to plan and allow for these adventures simply for the sake of my joy. *Not* at the expense of my work or my parenting. *But in addition to those things.*

I wanted to be happy for my kids more often. I wanted to role model joy. I wanted to consciously choose play and not feel guilty about it. I wanted to live the lesson I just learned: the time you spend with your family, with your friends, or at work is way more about the quality than the quantity. *Whatever you are not changing, you are choosing.* I wanted to show up for everything in my life from a higher energetic space.

I did not plan it, but this shift in attitude inspired my kids. I showed them that it's okay to take time for yourself, and it's important to have a passion, hobby, or the space to do what you love. They began to internalize the importance of prioritizing their health and happiness.

As the idea of allowing myself to "play more" sunk in, I heard about a non-sanctioned run called "Rim to Rim to Rim." It's a 46-mile endurance challenge across the Grand Canyon and back—in one day. The trails include over 20,000 feet of elevation change and intimidating, sometimes dangerous, switchbacks and drop-offs.

The idea flew into my mind and stuck to it like flypaper. I dreamed I could do it.

And yet, I had never run a marathon before.

I just loved the idea of it: exploring the outdoors, having a reason to train hard, and an excuse to force me back into shape while taking on a personal challenge.

Facing that challenge made me feel more alive at 40 than I felt in my 20s and 30s.

I trained for months, and it was not easy to balance the training with my work and family commitments. At Apple Seeds, we had just launched the national franchise business for our kids' music program. My twins were now nine, and my son was four. Like so many parents, I felt there were too many demands and not enough time or energy. Some days I felt completely overwhelmed and not sure how to make it all work. But when I felt that guilt creep back in, I would remind myself how my kids just wanted me to be happy and ask, "What is the story I want to tell with my life?"

I'd hear my older self begging me to make the most of the time I had. To accept the challenges that might help me grow. To let go of the small stuff. To recognize that play and fun were as important as my ambitions and successes. In fact, without joy, not much else mattered.

We all play in different ways. The key is to define what you love to do for yourself and then make time for it.

WHAT IS PLAY ANYWAY?

Play is the missing ingredient in your overall self-care. For years, I've worked with my coaching clients to focus on self-care, including helping them start a meditation practice, initiate healthy sleep routines, or shift their nutrition and exercise patterns.

What I've found over the years, though, is that to truly take care of your whole self and to feel more joy and meaning, you must also prioritize play. The latest scientific research shows the same thing. We simply need to re-educate ourselves about play and learn to have fun again. Then we need to allow ourselves to do it. Our mental health is at stake.

But I don't mean "play" the way you might think of it for kids.

I mean play for adults.

I've spent 20 years working in the area of play. First at UNICEF, creating and managing sport and play programs in countries on nearly every continent. I saw first-hand how these programs protected children by keeping them in safe spaces and off the streets and taught them life lessons so crucial to their well-being. I witnessed how play helped people retain a sense of hope, especially amid crisis or conflict.

Years later, I co-founded Apple Seeds, and we catered to thousands of neighborhood families in our indoor playground. I wrote curricula for kids based on the concept of "learning through play." In short, my life's work has been all about play.

That is why when I started my life coaching business, I noticed that play is the missing ingredient for so many of my clients. Obviously, health, relationships, finances, and work are critical. Yet even when people have these in order, they still feel stuck. They can't seem to shake the malaise, especially in mid-life. It's like they've lost their sense of fun on the path to adulthood, and they long for something more. I've come to understand not only what this "something more" is, but that it's already right inside of them.

It's play.

Play is purposeless and done for its own sake—or rather, the only specific result of play is *joy*. Your joy. Play has no economic significance and doesn't necessarily lead to praise or recognition. Play is voluntary and has an inherent attraction. In play, there is a freedom from time and a continuation desire. What's more, you have a diminished consciousness of self when you play, and you are immersed in the present moment. In this context, play is far from frivolous.

Let's be frank. How often do you feel that way? When you look back on this past week, month or year, how often have you lost track of time? How often do you laugh and feel lighter because you are engaging in something you love to do? Be honest. How many times do you choose to do something just for you or for your own sense of fun?

Exhaustion too easily becomes our way of being, and our net worth can easily define our self-worth. Yet deep down, we crave contentment, satisfaction, and fulfillment.

Sophisticated studies—research involving brain mapping, for instance—show us that play lowers anxiety and, at the same time, fosters creativity. Engaging in playful activities can improve productivity and elevate your level of energy. I was trained as a master practitioner in energy in my coaching certification school, and I promise you that play is the fast track to a higher energy space where joy resides. Play helps you decrease stress, tap the present moment, and improve your sleep, all simultaneously. These facts are backed by science. Does this help convince you to start playing now, or at least add play to your to-do list?

Playing more doesn't mean you shirk your responsibilities or ignore your ambitions. It's about staying responsible, focused, and successful, but at the same time prioritizing yourself and having a little more fun along the way. You have just one life, one shot at this! Are you making the most of it?

To live with more joy and meaning, you have to shed the guilt and stop equating success with seriousness. You have to come to terms with society's expectations of what you are *supposed to do* or who you are *supposed to be*. You have to define what it is you love to do and then go do more of it. It's not just fun; it's essential.

As Dr. Stuart Brown, the renowned expert on play, writes, "the opposite of play isn't work. It's depression."

WHAT IS YOUR PLAY PERSONA?

The good news is that we all have a play persona, and it's easy to discover (or rediscover) the ways you like to play. It takes a mindset shift and some knowledge about the ways you can channel your sense of play. Using scientific research and real-life stories from my coaching clients, I developed five primary play personas.

1. *The Mover* enjoys physical activity and finds joy in walking, hiking, running, yoga, swimming, tennis, or other athletic pursuits.

2. *The Thinker* is happiest with cerebral stimulation and enjoys reading, learning a new language, or engaging in games like cards, chess, or crossword puzzles.

3. *The Creator* derives joy from making things. Happiness is found through the act of creation, whether it be painting, scrapbooking, photography, or writing.

4. *The Connector* is someone who feels fulfilled when connecting with others, be it eating dinner out with friends, performing in a concert, or telling jokes.

5. *The Explorer* craves novelty and finds joy in the newness of experiences, from traveling to new places, making collections to jog the mind, or visiting museums and learning.

Where do you see yourself? Which of these personas define you? We each have a little of all of them in us, though one or two usually stand out as predominant and express our greatest sense of fun and enjoyment. I am equally a Mover and an Explorer, with a heavy dose of Connector too.

I want to help you let go of your guilt, take time for yourself, and discover exactly how you like to play. Then I want you to believe that you will begin to get unstuck by playing more, tapping the present, and choosing joy. It's comforting, almost spiritual, knowing that indeed there is more than this. What could be more freeing than radical self-expression and doing what you love?

THE TOOL

First, you need to pause before you play.

It's helpful to get out a pen and paper since writing solidifies your thinking. Your wish is like sending an invitation to the universe.

Take your time answering these ten questions. They are intended to help jog your mind on how you have fun and get closer to understanding your play persona. Smiling is encouraged!

1. When was the last time you lost track of time?

2. What did you use to do that made you happy, but you are no longer doing?

3. Why did you stop?

4. What do you do for fun now for you and no one else but you?

5. What percent of your day is allocated to personal enjoyment?

6. How guilty do you feel when you are having fun or doing something for yourself?

7. How much fun or happiness do you think you "deserve?"

8. How upset do you think others will feel when you take time for yourself to play?

9. How did you play as a child?

10. What are your hobbies?

Now, make a list of three activities you would like to do more of, such as gardening, playing pickleball, doing crosswords, or going on a hike. Make it yours. Even if cleaning out your kitchen drawers makes you happy, write it down. Just be authentic, be you. Dig deep. Remember, the only goal is your joy.

1. _____

2. _____

3. _____

Now, revisit the list above. Did you write things you think you *should* be doing for fun, as expected by society or the people around you? Or are the activities from that space in your heart? In other words, your list should follow these three simple rules:

1. When you think about your play activity before you do it, it should excite you.

2. When you actively do it, it should energize, not drain you.

3. Afterward, it should make you feel lighter and more whole, not guilty for taking the time.

Now, revisit your activities based on the above rules and mostly ensure they can be included in your life *right now*. They should fulfill your deepest sense of play and bring you fun and enjoyment. Re-write them here:

1. _____

2. _____

3. _____

Now that you have your play activities, what is your play persona? Can you guess it based on the above?

To find out exactly what percent of your soul is a Mover, Thinker, Creator, Connector, or Explorer, take my **Play Quiz!** You can find it on my website at www.alisonqualter.com/playquiz

You will immediately receive personalized results, as well as a **Playlist** with suggested activities to help get you started.

I can also work with you more deeply to help get you unstuck and define specific ways to add more play and breathe life into your days. You can explore my group coaching workshops, **Press Play on Life** at www.alisonqualter.com, or contact me directly for 1:1 support at alison@alisonqualter.com

I am here to help you. I deeply believe that you were brought into this world to shine your light and squeeze the most out of this one chance you've been given. You *can* have more than this. As Mary Oliver asks, "What is it you want to do with your one wild and precious life?"

I can't wait to meet you.

Until then, stop reading and go play!

Alison Qualter is a personal and professional coach and founder of "Press Play on Life." She's an entrepreneur who co-founded two businesses with franchised locations, the executive in charge of sport and play for development globally at UNICEF, a former Associate Producer for *NBC News*, an athlete who has pursued endurance challenges on five continents to raise money for students who are blind, and most importantly, the joyful mother of three children. Alison has been profiled in *The New York Times, Forbes, Crain's, New York Magazine*, and more.

Before coaching, Alison and her partners created Apple Seeds, a play space for families with children newborn to 5-years-old, including an indoor playground, classes, boutique, and events. Founded in 2007, Apple Seeds had three locations in NYC, two in Dubai and Mumbai, and welcomed thousands of families. Songs for Seeds, their educational music program, was franchised to 32 locations and is offered online.

Before this, Alison worked for UNICEF, creating the global Office of Sports for Development and managing partnerships with FIFA, IOC, and others. Alison mainly traveled to sub-Saharan Africa to use sport and play in education, health, and child protection programs.

Before UNICEF, Alison worked in TV news, starting at NBC for TODAY and became an Associate Producer at *Dateline*.

Alison has a MPA from Princeton University and BA in Psychology from Boston College.

Alison, an avid traveler, has visited over 75 countries. She is a Certified Professional Coach with iPEC, an Energy Leadership Index Master Practitioner, a certified mindfulness trainer, and has an advanced yoga practice.

She enjoys handstands, hiking, and her three great kids.

To learn your Play Persona, take the Play Quiz at www.alisonqualter.com/playquiz

To have Alison help you get unstuck and prioritize play, check out her programs at www.alisonqualter.com or follow Alison here:

IG: @alisonqualter

FB: www.facebook.com/AlisonQualter

LinkedIn: https://www.linkedin.com/in/alison-qualter-berna-9a194931/

CHAPTER 18

A CANCER DIAGNOSIS

HOW IT HELPED ME
DRAW MY LINES IN THE SAND

Lynne Fletcher O'Brien

MY STORY

My story is not unique. All too many people face this personally or with a friend or a loved one. I think I almost thought this would eventually happen to me.

Our family of five took a trip to Africa, and I felt off. I couldn't sleep; I felt hot, lethargic, and just not myself. We arrived home, and that week I was driving on the highway and had to hold my eyes open with my hand to stay awake. I rarely get sick and thought that maybe I picked up something on the trip. Unconcerned, I made an appointment to go to an infectious disease doctor, thinking how exotic it would sound to say I had malaria or yellow fever from Africa. The doctor took many blood samples and ended by saying, "Sorry, I cannot do anything more for you." He sent me on my way with the number of a hematologist. I still felt pretty sure it was something routine. When the next doctor's office answered with, "Hello, Virginia Cancer Specialists," I didn't hear anything else other than the word cancer and felt my heartbeat loudly in my chest as the sweat trickled down my forehead. I learned that all hematologists are also oncologists, so I went to this appointment hoping for the best but stopped discussing my "blood issue" and silently hoped the kids and my husband wouldn't notice.

The day I was diagnosed with leukemia, a late Friday afternoon in February 2012, was a busy one. My doctor explained my test results in a cheerful tone, "You have a garden variety blood cancer—chronic Lymphocytic Leukemia (CLL). You have a great smile! And how was Africa? Did you get great photos?" *What is he talking about?* As he calmly explained that I needed a scan and more tests, the news did not sink in. I was not hearing that I had cancer. My mind was swirling with all I needed to do at home. The kids were getting off the bus shortly. I had dinner to prepare for arriving-any-minute cousins and a busy sports schedule for my children that weekend. My husband was stuck on a runway in New York. And, as usual, my phone was dead. I didn't have time for leukemia. As I drove home, the realization of what he said began to take hold. Slowly, I imagined my life would change forever.

I had cancer.

I also was thinking about my mother-in-law, who died the previous year from leukemia within weeks of her diagnosis, and my grandmother, who died forty years ago within weeks of her leukemia news. I felt a chill thinking about this word that led to no good endings.

I tried to remain calm when I got home and while greeting our guests and while preparing lasagna. But finally, during our dinner, after the kids left the table, I blurted out to my husband and our guests, "Oh, I meant to say that at my appointment today, they told me I have leukemia." This is not a suggested way to make this kind of announcement.

I had the weekend to think this over. I called my primary doctor, and he expressed skepticism as this disease is usually found in older males. I called a college roommate, a physician, who connected me with a national specialist I could see the following week in Boston. I remember that cloudy, raw day sitting in the waiting room with my husband as one of the darkest of my life. With my husband gripping my hand and both of us not saying much, we observed the hairless and sick people around me, heard the cries from patients and their families, and smelled that antiseptic hospital odor. This doctor confirmed the diagnosis but explained, "It's a chronic condition that we don't have to treat right away. We'll be in a "watch and wait" mode," which I quickly began to call "watch and worry." He assured me that many people live long lives with this and die of other causes. But because I was so young, almost turning 50, it would be more serious.

From that day to this one, I became a patient, then an advocate, a fighter, a fundraiser, and an expert on my cancer, and now even an entrepreneur. I began what is now a ten-year journey to save my own life, trying to understand blood counts, chemotherapy, endless doctor visits, and a reverence for the word "remission," which I have yet to hear.

But first, I went into a full-blown panic. For months, I didn't tell my parents or children (then 11, 15, and 16). *How would I tell them, and what would I say?* I finally had to tell my parents, and when my dad answered, he knew it was bad news once he heard my voice and cried, "No, no, no." I will never forget the sound of desperation in his cry. I finally told my children the way I was instructed online. I was to bring them all together so that they could hear the same thing at once. I told them that my "blood issue" was actually leukemia and that I was seeing the best doctors, so they didn't need to worry, and nothing was changing now. My older two tech-savvy children said they already knew this news as "it is on every computer and all my browsing history." No one asked very much, and life went on.

Since this was chronic and we were watching it, I had no surgery and no treatment. *So what was I supposed to tell everyone else? How can I not alarm them? What am I even telling them; that I have this disease and have no idea what is ahead. I have no plan, no idea, and I don't know how sick I will get?*

At times I found myself wishing I had another cancer so I could deal with it and all the support that goes with it and move on. But I kept hearing that I was lucky to have this disease, even with the emotional strain. So I braved on and pushed it to the corners of my mind best as I could. I slowly told friends, which was exhausting. And when they asked how to help, I had no idea what to say. Sometimes I wanted people to ask how I was doing, and other times I didn't. I know everyone was worried. I cried a lot when I was alone and cried through an entire wedding weekend, thinking, *would I see my kids married? Will I meet their spouses and my grandchildren? Will I even see them graduate from high school?* I managed to avoid researching or reading about CLL for months. I also ironically made clear to my husband and friends I wasn't going to be one of those women who wore pink and had a team of support.

Four years later, my blood got to levels where the doctor concluded it was time to start chemotherapy. The whole process was much easier than I feared, and though I didn't achieve remission, the drug did improve my blood. And four years later, my blood again dropped to those low levels, and I'm now on a pill that didn't even exist when I was diagnosed. Again, I am improving but not in remission. Through it all, the worrying and the unknown has been the worst part. This disease makes me immune-compromised, so COVID amped up my anxiety. My friend and I, who also has CLL, joke that there is a chance we will live until 100 and will feel we wasted our whole lives worrying.

THE TOOL

So how am I getting through this? My suggestions and tools apply to anyone with an illness or issue of any kind. But whatever you do, it has to be authentic to you.

Get involved and build community: At the dentist's office a few months after my diagnosis, I saw a brochure about a half marathon for women with the proceeds going for leukemia research, and I honestly hoped it had already happened as I didn't know if I could do it. I made some calls, found out it was two months away and decided to do it alone. I had to prove to myself I was still healthy enough to do this, and it would give me a reason to stay healthy. I didn't ask anyone to run with me in case I couldn't do it or didn't follow through. This was my issue, and I'd deal with it alone.

So one early Saturday, I went to practice held by The Leukemia and Lymphoma Society (LLS), and the first thing before stretching was the "mission moment" to help learn why we were doing this. The person who spoke was the first person I met who had my cancer. I joined her team, trained with her, and ran the race with her. Right then, I learned my first lesson; the value of finding and building the right community. I now know over twenty people with my disease, and we alternate helping each other and being helped.

The next year I decided to go with a team. We had about thirty of my friends and the following year a team of almost one hundred. Altogether, we raised over a million dollars for the cause. I guess you could say I did end up as a woman running with a team, though in purple, not pink!

I learned this group effort was a way to talk to friends and family. Our Team LOL (Love our Lynne) was a great community for me and provided me with so much support. Initially, it was hard asking for money as it felt selfish, but I knew everyone is affected by cancer, and this money would ultimately help all cancers. I used to joke in my talks and toasts that cancer was fun! We had cocktail parties, early morning walks, home shopping parties, fundraisers, auctions, and guest bartender nights. Through this event and organization, I met so many new people and became so much closer to all of my friends. This community continues to be my life support.

Learn to communicate: I had the chance to speak many times and share my story. At one event before race day, the organizers asked all cancer survivors to stand, and I joked out loud, seated next to my daughter, "I'm not sure I survived yet." She ran out of the room crying, and I realized I screwed up big time. As it turned out, she wasn't upset about my survivor comment but didn't realize I actually had cancer. I told my kids I had a blood issue and leukemia but never said the word cancer. This was a regrettable mistake, and I learned to be more transparent after that.

I have learned to communicate in the best way possible. It's not easy, but it's important to say things such as, "I appreciate your asking how I am all the time, but I will let you know when anything changes." I realize it's also a gift to others and to myself to say, "Yes, you can help me; here is what I need." I know how great I feel when people let me help them, accompany them to an appointment, buy them flowers or watch their dog. Yet, it was hard for me to say yes for a long while. Equally, I also have learned that it's perfectly acceptable to say no.

Again, you have to be authentic to yourself. For me, I preferred to go to chemo and infusions alone as it felt like a bigger deal with people. Alone it felt like it never happened.

See the best in others: I made a decision from the beginning not to get upset no matter what people say and just assume it's coming from a good place. Negative energy is not helpful. My dad once told me after I had a fight with a friend as a child that I should forgive people and assume that, in general, people just don't know what to say. So, for example, when I tell someone about my cancer, and they respond with a story of a friend who died of cancer or how they feel lucky that they are in perfect physical health, I should just assume they're expressing their fears and are well-intentioned.

Advocate and learn: Almost exactly four years later from my diagnosis, on the night of January 12, 2016, just months after finishing my last chemo treatment and feeling cautiously hopeful, I settled in to watch President Obama's final State of the Union address. And for the second time, the word cancer was about to change my life. The President announced and spoke of his new Moonshot effort and said, "For the loved ones we've all lost, for the families that we can still save, let's make America the county that cures cancer once and for all."

I jumped up off the couch with tears of joy in my eyes, I texted my friends about it and so many shared thoughts of those they lost or those who were struggling. So many were asking, "What can we do?" Since my own diagnosis, the sense of helplessness I felt was replaced with hope and a tremendous calling. I felt like the President was speaking to me, and I was up for the challenge.

That night I made a decision to do whatever I could do to make this challenge a reality. I didn't know how or what I was going to do, but I was going to do it. I called everyone I could think of and finally got a job. I loved every minute of helping bring people together and organizing ways for "everyday Americans" to help. My most meaningful project was calling the Navajo Nation; they told me no one had ever called them back before. Through the work of many, this eventually led to the opening of the first cancer care for Native Americans anywhere in the county. And I was lucky enough to go to the ribbon cutting a few years later with Jill Biden. Through this experience, I learned it truly is better to give than to receive.

Serve others: As a result of my Moonshot experience, I was also asked to be on the national boards of LLS, the Prevent Cancer Foundation, and the Cancer Support Community. Through these positions, I have been able to not only give of my time and help fundraise, but I have been able to mentor patients and help them navigate through a cancer diagnosis. If I had known about these organizations when I was diagnosed, I might not have made the mistakes I did. These organizations also helped me further build my community that supports me.

Start a business: A big blow to me was the news from my doctors that not only did I have cancer, but I would be susceptible to other cancers, especially melanoma. My favorite thing in life is to be by on the water or in the water, boating or walking the beach. I realized I had to find a solution. And also many friends didn't want to go to the beach because they didn't want to wear a suit. I felt more urgency than ever to live my life without regret. I thought I would draw my line in the sand and get out there and get others in the water. I had no fashion experience but decided to make my own line of water-wear sunproof accessories. I realized the tools I used to get me through this cancer journey were also my lines in the sand. So I, of course, named my company Line in the Sand.

Think of yourself as a survivor: I thought a lot about that survivor question so many years after that question was posed. And I decided that you are a survivor the day you decide to fight for yourself and others and not let cancer (or any other disease or issue) win. Being a survivor is when you learn to live your life.

You don't always need to be positive: Everyone wants to give me the positive spin, but I don't always need that, and in fact, being positive all the time can be toxic. I think it's healthier with any setback to live through the emotions and feel the pain. It is okay to feel sad and scared and not know the next step. Sometimes I appreciate it more when someone says, "That must be scary for you," or "How are you handling this?"

Learn to accept setbacks: I have had many ups and downs and have viewed them as a natural course of things. I ended up in the hospital two times and have had some delays in treatment due to side effects. But for me, it is best to accept that there will be setbacks. We have no control over so much in life, including our health.

Try new things: Doing things that scare me and learning new skills help me feel alive. Initially, it was running a half marathon, jumping out of a plane, and taking kite-boarding lessons, but later it was my policy job, starting a business, pitching my company, and even writing this chapter!

While I have yet to achieve remission, I'm hopeful of the future and that I will continue to have new treatments available for my leukemia. While I "worry and wait" for remission or a cure, I have learned the best thing I could do for myself was to create a meaningful life on my terms.

Lynne O'Brien's career in health care over the past thirty years has been in the private, public and non-profit sectors. As a lawyer, health care and patient advocate, and cancer survivor, she understands challenges in the health care field from various viewpoints.

She began her career as a lawyer representing pharmaceutical and health care companies. She later worked for the DuPont Merck joint venture and eventually ran the DuPont Pharmaceuticals government affairs office in Washington D.C., leading health care policy and legislative efforts at the state and federal level for over ten years.

Lynne was diagnosed with leukemia in 2012 and, since then, has been a tireless advocate for cancer research and patient advocacy. In 2016 she served as a Policy Analyst for the Cancer Moonshot. In that role, she did outreach to health care organizations and helped involve "everyday Americans" to become involved in the effort. Since leaving the Moonshot at the end of the Obama administration, she has continued the work started there in the private sector. She currently serves on three national boards: The Leukemia Lymphoma Society (LLS), Cancer Support Community, and Prevent Cancer Foundation.

In 2019 Lynne started an online company, Line in the Sand, manufacturing water wear including leggings, tops, dresses, rashguards, and other accessories. These products empower women to be outside and feel comfortable and covered in the water or for other activities. 100% of the profits are given to cancer and ocean organization.

A graduate of Princeton University in Political Science, and the Georgetown University Law Center, Lynne lives in Northern Virginia with her husband, Greg O'Brien, CEO of the Americas for JLL. They are the proud parents of three grown children.

Find and follow Lynne here: www.lineinthesand.com

Instagram @line_in_the_sand

LinkedIn http://www.linkedin.com/in/lynne-fletcher-o-brien-337a64113

CHAPTER 19

HOW TO UNPACK

FIND THE MEMORIES HIDDEN IN YOUR TRAVEL COLLECTIONS

Jamie Edwards

"One day, you'll leave this world behind.
So live a life you will remember."

—Avicii, Swedish D.J.

MY STORY

I grip the cold, hard, metal handle of my X-Acto knife. *Zzzzzzzzzzt.* The number ten blade slices easily through the glossy, brown tape.

This sound is a familiar one by now. I rip into box number eight, labeled: 'House Stuff.' I would be annoyed by the lack of clarity, but for the fact that the handwriting is so obviously my own.

Cardboard flaps crack open, and I robotically reach in to grab yet another newspaper-swaddled object. My fingers are smudged with newsprint from *The New York Times*, which is fitting because that's exactly where my mind is—New York.

I unwrap the layers. IRAQ TO REVIEW HUSSEIN'S EXECUTION. BLOOMBERG SEEKS FURTHER CHANGES FOR CITY SCHOOLS. COURT TO OVERSEE U.S. WIRETAPPING IN TERROR CASES. Sensational headlines flash before my eyes, as do subheads, photos, and captions from my old life.

Balls of crumpled paper pile up as I expose what lies inside. I feel the chipped paint before I see it. The rim is rough to the touch, the surface uneven, like cracked earth. Its outer shell is a macro view of fractured tectonic plates. Once a vivid ultramarine, the color has dulled, and I see original stoneware clay beneath the surface. I hold it at arm's length and consider the other shades of blue, cornflower, cobalt, and cerulean, among them.

I behold my treasure—a small, ceramic bowl. In a word, it's beautiful.

Then I blink, and my mind returns. I'm in Tokyo. I live here now.

FINDING A NEW SPACE

My surroundings come into focus. Blank white walls, highly polished wooden floors, and crystal-clear windows. An empty apartment, in a new city, in a new country, on a new continent. I'm unsettled. Out of my comfort zone and time zone, simultaneously. *My kids*, I think to myself, *will smear the windows within an hour.*

The bowl in my hand is from Mexico. It has traveled with us from New York to Tokyo. We found it in a gritty backstreet pottery shop in Todos Santos, where we also bought a hand-painted ceramic sink. Who buys a sink in Mexico? From the look of it then, every tourist in Todos Santos.

I remember my husband awkwardly carrying the sink through the airport. It was tightly wrapped in an old edition of *El Diario de Mexico*. While he looked ridiculous, he wasn't alone. I'd counted other men sheepishly carrying sinks, stuffing them into overhead bins.

Our Mexican sink is long gone. However, this bowl in my hand, and the amusing memories it conjures up, remain.

Gently, I place the bowl upon the long, built-in shelf beside me and unwrap the next one. It's warm in my inky hands, having spent days boxed up in a stifling customs warehouse in Yokohama. I feel its energy. Then, continue to unload the remainder of box number eight: ten more bowls, ten more memories.

One by one, I add them to the shelf.

STARTING OVER, AGAIN

Allow me a few steps backward. Barefoot steps. This is Japan, after all.

I moved to Tokyo in January of 2007 with a husband, two kids, and our life's belongings. It turns out, our life's belongings fit into 22 cardboard boxes. Boxes that spend two weeks crossing the Atlantic Ocean in a Maersk shipping container—boxes with more useless labels, like 'Kids,' 'Misc.,' and 'Stuff.'

The story I tell is committed to memory. "We moved to Tokyo for my husband's job," I chirp automatically when asked.

But that's not the whole story. We wanted an adventure and to explore a part of the world that had been far out of reach. If I hadn't said yes, I would've spent my life regretting it. My kids, aged six months and two years old, had no say in the matter.

Before I blink, we are boarding British Airways Flight BA5 to Tokyo. The unmistakable scent of stuffy, recirculated air follows me to my seat. *Sayonara*, New York.

TREASURE HUNTING

Our years in Asia fuel my travel obsessions, as well as my travel collections. Ceramic bowls are not my only vice. I spent years eating and drinking my way through New York City restaurants and bars, picking up branded matchboxes along the way. They sit in tall, glass vases in the living room, where every so often, I dump them out to relive a great meal. By the time we leave Tokyo, I need more vases.

Shells found on remote beaches, in places like Mauritius, Bora Bora, and Vietnam, line the ledge of my bathtub. I look closely at one of my favorites from Thailand, which I have since discovered is called *Cabrit's Murex*. It's a spectacular shell in a collection of spectacular shells.

It spirals from the bottom up like a scoop of soft-serve ice cream on a sugar cone. The swirls of color are distinctly maple pecan. It has a long, delicate tail that narrows to a sharp point, and ten tiny spines jut out randomly. It's a marvel. Mother Nature is a masterful artist.

The reason I love admiring this shell is more than its outer beauty. It brings me back to our family vacation on Koh Samui. I smile, remembering how I accidentally booked it during the rainy season. Stormy beach walks, soggy Pad Thai noodles, and slippery elephant rides. It's funnier now than it was then, trust me.

Yet, even travel mistakes lead to entertaining memories. In fact, they often do. "I'll never ride an elephant again!" my five-year-old daughter howled. *You and me both*, I thought.

Over three years in Japan, our bowl collection grows, with additions from Bhutan, Cambodia, and Turkey. Memories of trekking to the Tiger's Nest, photographing Angkor Wat at sunrise, and haggling at The Grand Bazaar, flood my mind. The shelf is crowded—each bowl vying for its own space. My mind is crowded, too.

I seek out more space for both.

THE THRILL OF THE HUNT

These collections have power. And allow me to relive family vacations, much in the same way a photograph might do for someone else. Collections connect me to a period in my life, like the traditional Japanese *kokeshi* dolls I amassed for my daughter while living abroad.

Collections can be passed down from an older generation and summon childhood memories. My grandmother collected elephants (trunks up only, for good luck), and as kids, my sister and I loved to hunt for them around her house. The shaggy, wall-to-wall carpet felt thick beneath me as we crawled like elephants in search of water.

I still see those jade, malachite, and stone pachyderms with total clarity. I love holding these images in my mind and remembering her through them.

For me, it's the thrill of the hunt—the excitement of finding a treasured addition to my collections. Every time I grab a new matchbox from a hostess stand, I cheer like I've won the lottery. My husband finds it embarrassing. I don't care.

EVERY OBJECT TELLS A STORY

'Brrrrrrrr,' my hands are frozen. It's August. Winter in South Africa.

We are at the Old Biscuit Mill in Cape Town, which is deserted, dark, and cold. I check my watch—8:55pm. We are dangerously close to missing our dinner reservation. I'm on edge. I'm never late.

Just ahead, I see light. But, it's not from the restaurant we're seeking. From the darkness, I cup my hands and peer into the window like a child. What I see beyond the glass ignites my senses. Bowls, vases, vessels, and other ceramics, are on display in this brightly lit showroom—begging me to enter. I try the knob. But, alas, the studio is closed for the night.

I vow to come back tomorrow. A few steps away, we find the restaurant's entrance. A warm glow escapes from the door; it's 9:02 pm. We made it.

Imiso Ceramics is owned by two South African artists, Zizipho Poswa and Andile Dyalvane. While different in style, they complement each other effortlessly. By a stroke of artistic luck, they are together in the showroom when we arrive the next day. Both exude an inner calm I could spend years trying to achieve.

Meeting Zizi and Andile makes choosing only one bowl a challenge. As a rule, we buy one bowl from our travels. I'm a rule follower (even if it is my own rule). Sometimes we find none, but never two.

However, we've never had the opportunity to meet an artist behind any of our pieces until now. I ask about their inspiration and technique and watch their faces light up as they talk about their craft.

Unsurprisingly, we buy two bowls. They get wrapped up in *The Daily Sun* and shipped to our house in D.C.

The first bowl is a hand-pinched piece from Zizi. Her work is inspired by the traditional Xhosa textiles of her childhood. The bowl I'm drawn to has razor-thin, symmetrical, black lines. The lines fan upwards from the base to the rim as if applied with a surgeon's precision. Metallic bronze paint drips down the sides, smooth to the touch. The interior is blood red. It feels alive.

Second, a bowl from Andile's 'Scarified' collection. It celebrates scarification, a tribal form of body art performed when it was thought that black skin couldn't be tattooed. Andile masterfully treats the clay as if it's skin, and in doing so, recreates the patterned bodies of his youth.

The 'skin' of the bowl I hold in my hand is slashed and reveals hints of red and blue paint underneath. If this treatment is meant to create tension and drama, it succeeds on both fronts.

I admire how each bowl holds the intensity of the artist's past within it. They express the stories of Zizi and Andile's heritage. For me, they hold travel memories. One of which is the serendipity of finding them on a chilly night at the Old Biscuit Mill when we nearly missed our dinner reservation.

PACKING MATTERS

In 2010, we move back to the United States. The bowls, which have doubled in number, get wrapped and repacked—this time in *The Asahi Shimbun*. The 12-point *hiragana*, *katakana*, and *kanji* characters are now quite familiar, and I'm nostalgic.

Our matchbox collection has also grown, serving as a reminder of culinary experiences in Singapore, Hong Kong, and Bali. Gastronomic records of unusual dinners. Like the time we ate chicken sashimi in a hidden back-alley restaurant in Nakameguro. To answer your questions, "Am I glad I tried it?" Sort of. "Would I eat it again?" No, never.

We receive a packing memo that clearly states shipping matches is strictly prohibited. How can I leave decades of my mini-treasures behind? Ever the rule follower, I become a rule breaker, just this once, by hiding the matches in socks, shoes, and shoeboxes.

What if the Maersk shipping container spontaneously combusts on its passage to the United States? I panic, then google 'explosions at sea' every day for two weeks. My hair turns gray. Karma.

FINDING COMFORT IN TRAVEL MEMORIES

The matchboxes arrive without incident, but our new life in D.C. is a circus. Chaotic in the way only parents of small children can understand. I juggle rec soccer, multiplication tables, and dentist appointments. I bounce between the aisles of Safeway to produce balanced meals—making sure we have enough real fruit on hand to offset the fruit roll-ups.

Laundry is constant, as my kids are messy and participate in sports that stain clothes in ways I can never eliminate. Life is a mental and physical blur. Where's my personal space? It doesn't matter, as I've forgotten I need it.

It's a decade spent tending to my family and ignoring my travel collections. Although I pass them daily, I don't see them, let alone listen to what they have to say.

Then, March 2020 happens.

REDISCOVERY

Housebound, along with the rest of the world, I look for ways to see the 'silver lining' everyone is talking about. I'm encouraged to use the pandemic as a chance to reset. To slow down. To pay attention to things I hadn't been paying attention to before. *Was I not paying attention?* I can't remember.

I try meditation, which is healthy for the mind and soul, with the added advantage of taking up time in days that often feel never-ending. I've meditated off and on for years but am not motivated. I have a habit of running through my to-do list and wondering what to watch on Hulu during my practice. From what I understand about meditation, this is highly frowned upon.

Eventually, I get better about settling my mind since my to-do list shrinks. My appetite, unfortunately, doesn't.

I discover a room in my house that feels bright, even on rainy days. I sink into a corner chair like a well-oiled mitt cradling a baseball. Its supple leather grounds me. From there, large windows offer views of green grass, blue sky, and a red Japanese maple. Nature's primary color palette relaxes me. My physical space is redefined.

My mind has found space again, too.

On the way to my chair, I pass through the living room—the room that houses the things we've collected from our travels. How long had it been since I'd really seen them?

To anyone looking, my bowls are empty, and my shells and matchboxes are purely for display. I close my eyes and rediscover their stories. *This is my sacred space*, I think, as I remember how they got here from India, Colombia, and Iceland. Japan, Greece, and Croatia.

My eyes open. I'm in the same room, but I've changed.

The physical space where my collections live lead me to a sacred space within. Isn't that the ultimate goal—to find a sacred space inside ourselves?

Accessing that space is as easy as walking around the house.

THE TOOL

What do you collect? You may think you don't collect anything. I bet you're wrong.

I didn't realize we collected bowls until the day we packed up our life in New York. They'd been sprinkled around the apartment like family members scattered across the globe.

The discovery was thrilling. When I arrived in Tokyo, I found comfort in unpacking them. Like reuniting long-lost relatives. It made starting a new life in a foreign country easier to grasp and inspired me to expand my collection. I've since realized that anywhere my collections live is my sacred space.

TRAVEL AROUND THE HOUSE

Let's take a walk. You don't need shoes, as we aren't going far. Yet, we'll be covering a lot of ground. Keep your eyes open and your mind clear. Bring a journal.

Start in your bedroom; open drawers and closets. Consider the art on your walls. Do any artistic patterns emerge? Your very first collection may be hiding in plain sight. Passport stamps are tangible impressions of far-flung destinations located in one convenient little booklet.

Some of the best collections take up little space (at least physically). Postcards, postage stamps, luggage tags, and ticket stubs. Small reminders of big travels.

Tiptoe through your kids' bedrooms, stepping over piles of dirty laundry as you go. It sounds obvious, but collections usually come about organically. Maybe you've been buying old cameras for your daughter without realizing it. Or hats from baseball stadiums across the country.

Head downstairs. Sit in your favorite chair while you glance around the living room. The things you collect are a reflection of you. Is there a specific style of art you see or a collection you hadn't previously noticed?

A collection can be as many or as few pieces as you like. Whether three antique maps or 1000 shards of sea glass. Choose a place to show them off.

Frame maps, salon-style, on a large wall. Cluster sea glass inside a vintage display case. Stack oversized, glossy-paged travel books in the family room. Or, arrange *National Geographic* magazines, their signature honey-colored spines facing out, in the library. Grouping collections creates drama.

Remember how your collections began and the travel stories attached to them. Close your eyes and think about how they make you feel. Travel back in time. This is the heart of the matter, the emotional value of your collections. Savor them.

WRAPPING UP

Our kids are now in high school and will soon be off, finding their own space and perhaps, creating their own collections. My husband and I will eventually seek a new place to live and undoubtedly take our bowls, matchboxes, and shells—our precious travel memories—with us.

I have a stack of *The Washington Post* on standby.

YOUR TRAVEL MEMORIES ARE HIDDEN IN YOUR HOUSE

Let me help you find them. Download my free resource, *The Ultimate Guide to Starting a Travel Collection*, by going to https://www.iamlostandfound.com/guide

My guide lists creative collection ideas based on decades of travel. It illustrates ways a new collector can begin and ways a seasoned one can take their collections to a new level. Travel collections, while so personally valuable, often cost very little.

It's never too late to start collecting. I can help get you started. Safe travels.

Jamie Edwards is the creator of the adventure and luxury travel website *I am Lost and Found.*

Jamie's first-hand experiential writing style and stunning photography capture her life-long love of travel. Many of her readers look to her for off-the-beaten-path and adventure travel inspiration. They will often replicate her trips, knowing she has already done the legwork and research.

She is a regular guest on the highly acclaimed podcast, *TripCast360, 'The Ultimate Travel Podcast Experience,'* as well as a contributing writer for *A Luxury Travel Blog, CIRE Travel, Travel Curator,* and *Wellness & Wisdom Magazine.*

Yet, ultimately, Jamie is a collector. Whether passport stamps, shells, or memories. Collections tell her stories and inspire her travels.

Want Jamie's **FREE GUIDE**, The Ultimate Guide to Starting a Travel Collection? Visit https://www.iamlostandfound.com/guide for imaginative travel collection ideas and unique ways to display them.

Get ready to be inspired. Then, get lost.

www.iamlostandfound.com

Instagram @iamlostandfound_

CHAPTER 20

THRIVING FOR HARMONY

FLOWERS AND VASES

Hermon Black

MY STORY

"Hide your pain, and your pain will disappear." Those were the lessons I was taught growing up. I was never given the liberty to express stress or disappointments. I carry that with me to this day. I don't recommend it to anyone, as it could become a burden. It might make you feel suffocated. At least I feel that way somedays. But that wisdom is what drives me to always seek harmony.

One of the earliest traumas I faced was when my baby sister died of an accidental overdose on pills she mistook for M&Ms. I found her dumping them straight into her mouth from the pill bottle. I ran to our caregiver to tell her. I don't remember what I said. I was five years old at the time. But the reaction of our caregiver and the events that followed were confusing. I was sheltered from the scene and never given an explanation.

I remember my other sister and I were kept at my uncle's house so we wouldn't witness my parent's reaction. And later on, friends and family took turns sheltering us from facing the reality of it all. Everyone tiptoed around the topic. A week later, my grandmother kissed us and told us,

"God has chosen our baby sister to become an angel, and she will always protect us." That's where the conversation stopped. No one ever asked me what I saw. And I kept that memory to myself.

My mom continued to grieve behind closed doors. And when she wasn't behind that door, you did not see a trace of grief. Elegantly dressed with hair and make-up on point, she was pure radiance.

This major event in my life shaped my approach to pain and struggles. I closed myself off and did that quite well. I don't lock others out, but I don't volunteer to share. People accuse me of being closed off. And they get offended that I don't let them in. But what they don't understand is that it's my desire to have the space to go through the emotions on my own to get back to my harmonious space.

Harmony is food to my soul. It grounds me, and it gives me hope. In those tumultuous moments in my life, I dug into that space of harmony to gain the strength to overcome my anxiety. I believe in a Divine power and allowing the journey to take shape. My journey is nothing like I dreamt it. I so often admit that there were many unexpected setbacks.

In the early days of the pandemic, I started to experience depression like I have never before. It felt so hard to be motivated to dig into my tools to get out of the deepest, darkest places. It felt irrelevant to even think of flowers, which were my business.

When shipping as we know it came to a sudden stop and the supply chain was interrupted, I watched what happened to the cut flowers at the farms, to wholesale markets, and all that were in transit. With limited labor, the only option in the early days of the pandemic was just to put them behind the dumpster. That was a very hard reality for anyone in the flower world.

But it was in those hours that I felt the urge to connect with flowers and everything to do with them. I couldn't bear to think of all the hard work that went into growing these blooms and all the hope they could bring to people being totally lost.

Once I adjusted to the unique situation of the lockdown, I reached out to fellow florists and growers. We arranged times and dates to pick up while adhering to the COVID protocols, which were still new and very confusing. I applied every step to protect myself and those around me. I live right outside of DC, and most growers are at minimum a one-hour drive. That means I started driving those empty stretches of road weekly. Sometimes multiple times a week. That was life-changing for me. Not only could I see and touch flowers, but it also helped me to overcome my depression. I looked forward to the car ride, the farm visit, and to filling up my buckets with seasonal blooms.

On one of the first flower pick-up trips, I just walked around the farm quietly by myself. I felt light as if a weight was lifted off of my shoulders. I started to observe how each and every plant, tree, shrub, and flower were collaborating. I admired every inch of the farm and its surroundings. It filled me up with love and hope. I translated that energy of gratitude into the floral arrangements.

The joy I received from the simple trips reminded me what it means to do what you love. It made me see how we depend on one another. The interconnectedness of our existence is inevitable. Being passionate about our job and business empowers us and those around us.

A simple action of reaching into my positive energy and opening myself up to the possibilities led me to the most meaningful path.

I hope you enjoy the flowers around you, whether from your local market or the wildflowers in a field nearby. Here's a tool to help you appreciate the beauty of life in a flower.

THE TOOL

FLOWER MEDITATION

Any connection with nature is an incredible opportunity to slow down and celebrate a sacred space. When you "stop and smell the roses," you're literally basking in the presence of nature, which can instantly raise your vibration.

Here's a simple way to practice mindfulness meditation with a flower.

1. Find a flower from the local market, a field, or your backyard.

2. Notice the shape, size, and magnificent structure with your eyes. Notice its stem, leaves, and connections to other flowers. What do you see?

3. Gently hold the flower in your hands or fingertips. Notice how the petals or stems feel. What does the thickness of the petals feel like? Let yourself feel it. What do you feel?

4. Bring the flower to your nose and notice if it has an aroma. Breathe it in gently and slowly. Close your eyes and repeat. What do you smell?

5. As you're enjoying the flower, what do you hear? Notice any sounds of nature or sounds in the environment you're in.

Learning to listen to my emotions has been the key ingredient to overcoming my anxiety and stress. Flowers help! I keep seasonal fresh flowers in my home regularly. Having fresh flowers in your home not only enhances the room's aesthetic appeal but also reduces stress, brightens up your mood, increases creativity, and helps purify the air in your home.

Hermon Black is the founder of HB Fiori, a floral studio for events and subscription service in Arlington, Virginia. She has been featured in Arlington Magazine, Washingtonian, and NOVA Magazines. She loves learning and exploring the world of floriculture.

She is a proud mother of two boys.

Find and follow Hermon here:

www.hbfiori.com

Instagram: @hbfiori_hermonb

CHAPTER 21

FENG SHUI YOUR SOUL FIRST

HOW TO SET UP
YOUR SACRED WRITING SPACE

Laura Di Franco, MPT, Publisher

MY STORY

"Clear everything off your desktop. Deal with the clutter. File your papers and then dust off and clean all surfaces. The idea is to make some space so you can breathe and connect."

The first time someone coached me in Feng Shui, it was about decluttering. I remember Torrie telling me, "Clear everything from underneath your bed, and don't forget your stovetop; it's an abundance thing." I started and was instantly addicted. Not only was my house clean, but I could breathe better, and as I walked into the rooms, I smiled.

Okay Marie Kondo, I get the joy-sparking thing, now!

No, I never did get into the habit of rolling my shirts into little logs, but the joy is something I feel every time I look in my cupboards or closets now.

The next Feng Shui goddess I learned from was Dana Claudat. Holy decluttering and Feng Shui magic, y'all—this woman knows how to teach you skills that make checks show up in your mailbox. No joke.

I went through her decluttering boot camp and her Cash Catalyst course, and one spring day, after doing one of her meditations, I opened up an email I dreaded reading to find out from Bank of America that, "Your case has been resolved in your favor." That was a $2500 day for me. And a big win because I was involved in a scam that I decided to fight to the end. Little guy: 1, Big guy: 0.

Okay, there's something to this decluttering and Feng Shui thing. What else can I clean?

Another mentor, Honorée Corder, said, "Go clean your front door, and don't forget to clean your car!" After taking my bucket of warm, soapy water to the front door, I closed three business deals. That was a 30K win. And, my car? Well, I'm in the habit of washing Jamie regularly, so I already checked that off my list. Jamie is my 2016 shadow black Mustang eco-boost convertible. She doesn't stay dirty long.

Um, the money is flowing, and the amounts are getting bigger. I wonder what else is possible here?

I was hooked. And my house was really, really clean, which made me love living in it and decreased my stress because I could actually find the things I needed and used. Ease and joy became a regular feeling. And my Law of Attraction fans know like attracts like. Ease and joy, folks; we all want more of that! I was feeling it, big time, and getting more and more excited about the practice.

As a writer, I'm used to creating sacred writing spaces in my house. "Make the space you write be a place of ease and joy, where you love to go and sit to create. Think about what you put there and how you arrange the objects. Let this be an altar of sorts." This was Torrie again. I followed orders and had so many people call me "prolific" in terms of my writing afterward that I sat up a little straighter.

This Feng Shui thing goes for writing and my inner world, too!

When I told the world, "I write to Feng Shui my soul," I was speaking of cleaning my inner world, to clear a space for Divine words to flow through me. I started thinking of my external and internal spaces and how to clear and clean, opening a channel for connection, flow, and vibration of something bigger and more profound and magical. My writing shifted. I started not to have to think my way through it. My writing began to flow effortlessly. Inspired ideas were as close as me taking a deep breath and sitting down at my keyboard.

Whoa, I think I just channeled that poem!

Poetry has always been a thing for me. I've scribbled rhyming lines in my diaries since the age of fifteen. But it was a day in 2014, flying on a plane to Sedona, Arizona, to meet up with a bunch of healers, that I thought that channeling thing to myself for the first time. I connected to something much bigger than me who wrote (and later spoke) through me. That day was a life-changer. Making space for that connection became my practice, purpose, and passion.

Oh, I love that last line of alliteration, don't you?

> *"If you want to clean house, you must first see the dirt."*
>
> – Louise Hay

Louise may have been talking about her living room, but she was also talking about the limiting beliefs getting in the way of the flow. Connecting, cleaning, clearing, and making space for something new, whether it be words, money, or a job or relationship, means you have to be aware of the dirt first. The clutter in your closets is as important as the clutter in your mind. You need sacred space in both areas to be in full alignment with the Divine energy you are.

Sometimes I feel like the healing journey is about cleaning off the layers of that dirt. I think of a lantern with glass sides. It gets sooty after a while. Pretty soon, there's no light shining from the center. There can be layers and layers of dirt to clear off before the light of your essence shines out in a way you're illuminating the path for others.

I believe that journey is the human journey. Some of us have more dirt to clean off than others.

Creating sacred space in my home, and especially for my writing and creating, has been incredibly powerful, purposeful, satisfying, and outright magical.

"Mark, clean your door! I swear this works!" My mastermind colleagues and I, who have experienced the direct correlation of Feng Shui to receiving more money, urged our friend to do the cleaning. "My wife might just fall over if I started to clean," he joked back with us. My friend, Feng Shui Dana would say, "Clean your money corner!"

Money corner? Do I have a money corner?

It turns out both your home and every room in it have a money corner. Whoa, mind blown.

What the heck is in my money corners?

I wondered and then got to work. I even started to pay attention to the "corners" of my writing space and adorned them with crystals, placed ever-so-carefully to enhance the energy.

If you're still reading and not rolling your eyes at the crystal line, then good for you. That means your mind is open, and you're excited to find out what else is possible in terms of all of this!

Now, writers and creators, get ready because I'm going to give you a step-by-step for crafting your sacred writing space. May the Divine force of intentional Feng Shui magic be yours as you embark on this amazing journey.

THE TOOL

HOW TO SET UP YOUR SACRED WRITING SPACE

First of all, know this matters. Every space you live in matters. So if you're motivated after this chapter, go discover the information awaiting you. The rabbit hole on this one is real but powerful. Learn more about Feng Shui and decluttering strategies. Start small. Baby steps are better than no steps. Hence me starting you off with your writing space. My friend Dana Claudat of FengShuiDana.com has incredible resources for you. Then, when you're ready to publish your brave words for the world to read, I'm your gal.

What you need:

- A notebook and pen to write down what you see, feel, and want to change in your writing space.

- A non-toxic cleaner and rag for the dust
- A recycling bin for the paper
- A trash can for the junk
- Your favorite essential oils, objects, notebooks, candles, etc. to adorn your new space with

1. Survey your writing space. Where do you write and create? Do you have a dedicated, sacred space for this? If not, why not? If literal space is an issue, think about a sacred corner of a room where you can set up a small desk and chair. Decide on where your space is going to be.

2. Asses your seating. Your desk or table and chair should be comfortable and ergonomically set up, so your body is supported and relaxed. Increased tension in your shoulders, arms, back, and neck will shorten your ability to be in the flow. The physical therapist in me wants you to compare sitting posture for writing to a yoga pose. It's a therapeutic position that can enhance or hurt you. Make it a good one.

3. Assess your lighting. Great lighting is both an eyesight and an energy thing. How's the lighting in your writing space? Is there natural light? How can you increase that? Do lightbulbs need dusting off or changing? How about the light fixtures or lamps themselves? Clean it all and arrange better lighting for your workspace. Add candles and Himalayan salt lamps for extra magical juju.

4. Clean your desktop. I didn't hit you with this one straight away because this task can be daunting if you have some clutter. Grab your recycle bin, trash can, and cleaner and get to work. Clear all the clutter. Remove paper and objects you don't use or need and file papers in a filing cabinet or filing box that helps you feel organized. Once everything is off the desktop, clean it thoroughly before putting your items back. Make sure to clean and dust your computers, keyboards, microphones, and other electronics with appropriate tools, rags, and cleaners that don't damage them! Read the instructions if you don't know what to use.

5. Arrange useful objects within reach. If the writing space is easy to use and has all your favorite tools within arms reach, this will be a place

you love to sit. And that is the goal here! What do you use often? What can be kept in a drawer or cabinet? Try different arrangements until you love the way it feels.

6. Decorate with color and manifesting objects. You want your writing to feel inspired, easy, powerful, and prolific. So, does the decor in your room inspire you? Make you feel at ease? Help your flow? You can use paint colors, artwork, special pens, candles, books, quotes, or other sacred objects you love to inspire your writing space. Make this yours!

7. Privacy. When you write in a noisy room, the distractions can get in the way of your flow. Assess the location of your writing space to see if you need to change it up and create more quiet and privacy for your sacred writing time.

8. Speaking of distractions, get in the habit of unplugging before you write. Exit out of all other screens on your computer and make sure the notification noises are off. Put your phone somewhere you can't see the screen lighting up with texts. Turn the ringer off. If you have a landline phone, unplug it. If you have a person in your house who is famous for interrupting just when you get into the flow, make a little sign and post it outside your door: "Please be quiet, sacred writing in progress!"

9. Your writing time. Everyone is more productive during different times of the day, so figure out your best time for writing and creating, and then protect that time on your calendar. I hope you look forward to sitting in your sacred space as a VIP appointment with yourself. I'm an early morning person. When I don't honor that, my writing suffers or feels tight or constricted.

10. Extras. Do you love to write to music? What kind? Do you have a speaker that connects to your phone or computer so you can play your favorite inspirational music? How about that essential oil that helps you feel uplifted or inspired? I love my DoTerra oils! I change them out in my diffuser depending on my mood and goal for the day. Do you drink a special tea? How about brewing a cup before you sit to write? I love Tea Pigs teas. The "Happy" and "Calm" are two of my faves.

When you have a sacred writing space you love, your energy will be different (more joyful, easier, more relaxed), and that is the same energy you'll be infusing into your brave words. It's also the same energy your readers will feel when they read your beautiful writing. So, what do you want them to feel? Set up your sacred writing space to give you the advantage of helping *yourself* feel all those same things first! Your writing will never be the same! And your readers won't be able to put your writing down! Changing the world with your brave words starts with nourishing the sacred space for your writing. I can't wait to hear how it goes!

If you'd love more writing tips, please head over to https://BraveHealer.com and let me help you share your words with the world in a bigger way!

Laura Di Franco, MPT, is the CEO of Brave Healer Productions, where they publish world-changing wellness books. She spent 30 years in holistic physical therapy and 12 of those in private practice before pivoting to publishing and business strategy for healers. With 14-years of training in the martial arts and 25 books and counting, including 18 Amazon bestsellers, she's got a preference for badass in every way.

Her daily mission is to help fellow wellness practitioners do what they need to do to change the world in less time and with fewer mistakes and heartache on the journey. She shares her authentic journey, wisdom, and expertise with refreshing transparency and straightforward badassery. Hold on to your seat because riding alongside her means you'll be pushed into and beyond your comfort zone and regularly have way more fun with your purpose-driven fears.

When Laura chills out, you'll find her with a mojito at a poetry event with friends, driving her Mustang, bouncing to the beat at a rave, or on a beach in Mexico with something made of dark chocolate in her mouth. Joy is the way she healed herself.

Connect with Laura:

On her website: https://BraveHealer.com

On Facebook: https://www.Facebook.com/BraveHealerbyLaura

On Twitter: https://www.Twitter.com/Brave_Healer/

On Instagram: https://www.Instagram.com/BraveHealerProductions/

https://www.Instagram.com/BraveKidsBooks/

On LinkedIn: https://www.linkedin.com/in/laura-di-franco-mpt-1b037a5/

In her Free Facebook Community, Brave Badass Healers, a Community for World-Changers: https://www.Facebook.com/YourHighVibeBusiness/

CHAPTER 22

HONORING YOUR SACRED SPACE

Colleen Avis, Integrative Life Coach, Mindfulness Mentor, Yoga Guide

"There is no greater agony than bearing an untold story inside you."

– Maya Angelou

So often we imagine we are the only one who has experienced what we have, or our stories separate us and make us different from others. We believe if we told our stories others would judge us or not understand or relate.

The truth is, telling your story opens up the sacred space that offers opportunity to understand each other, connect, form bonds, and transform relationships. This sacred space invites us to connect deeper with ourselves, allowing space to make sense of experiences, and choosing how we want to evolve and grow. Sharing our stories and expressing ourselves help us connect our past, present, and future, looking at the positive and negative with limitless opportunity to explore how we tell our story and challenge if it's indeed the story we want to live in.

Our hope is the stories, approaches, and tools in this book offer you a sense of connection, a place to bond, and limitless possibilities for you to explore. We hope you are inspired to get curious and explore unique tools and approaches that support you as you cultivate your sacred space.

I have stories, one I have told myself and repeated for decades. For many years I allowed it to detach me from my sacred space and truest self. Many of my stories served me in the moment and others, the painful ones, have served me even more greatly. They were obstacles, but when viewed with a greater understanding and willingness to grow, were gifts of transformation and growth.

We all have stories, it's the meaning and power we give them and what we choose to do with them that matters. Your words matter. When we really listen and go within and turn up the volume on our intuition, the truth is there, our passion is there, and our big, bold, powerful purpose is there. It will guide us in the right direction. It is these spaces I know to be sacred. Your stories and experiences—you are a sacred space.

It's our innate nature and divine right to live our deepest purpose. The universe wants and needs you to share vulnerably and honestly, to shine your light and passion brightly.

You don't have to write your story in a book, or stand on a stage and speak to a large group to explore your sacred spaces, but we invite you to share your story, explore your experiences and the meaning you have given them, and be open to learn, choose, and grow.

As you explore and share your stories (with others or yourself) be curious about the spaces, in your mind, body and home, that are created or affected. So often we only see from a limited or one perspective—typically one we have always looked from—so I invite you to zoom out to see the larger picture or perhaps the picture from another perspective to honor the space you are in your home, your country, our world, our collective space, our universe.

Albert Einstein says, "A human being is a part of the whole called by the universe, a part limited in time and space. He experiences himself, his thoughts and feeling as something separated from the rest, a kind of optical delusion of his consciousness. This delusion is a kind of prison for us, restricting us to our personal desires and to affection for a few persons nearest to us. Our task must be to free ourselves from this prison by widening our circle of compassion to embrace all living creatures and the whole of nature in its beauty."

When we widen our view, we see our individual wholes are part of an intertwined larger whole. It is there that greater opportunity for growth and learning, and more importantly, love and compassion, thrives. Because when we see all our spaces and experiences are intertwined there is room for greater awareness and understanding.

As a group of authors we honor and accept you as the complete whole you are, nothing to fix, with limitless opportunities to be you!

If any of our stories have resonated with you, we invite you to reach out and connect with us, we would love to meet you and hear your stories. Know the story and tool we have each shared here is only a part of our sacred space and personal growth and expansion. It's a peek into our purpose, how we've created it and how we continue to cultivate and grow from it.

What I know is we all deserve happiness and it's there for you. It's in the spaces, the ones your uniqueness makes sacred that we invite our truest self to shine.

No matter your unique gift the world needs you to shine bright and create sacred space for yourself, that will naturally ripple to others.

It's from that space we invite you to find your unique way to embrace subtle shifts in mind, body and home that creates the life you deserve – full of purpose, love, joy and happiness.

HIRING A GUIDE

There's a reason you picked up this book and you are here now. Perhaps you feel like you're so close to getting your whole life together but can't quite get there. Maybe you feel stuck, in a cycle of negative patterns or you're feeling isolated and seeking connection. Perhaps you're searching for your purpose and hearing others stories and what worked for them in the journey of life helps you create your unique approaches and tools. Whatever your reason, I'm so glad you are here.

Each author in this book hopes someone reads their story and relates to them and feels inspired to find the subtle shifts that will create and enhance their sacred space. I encourage you to reach out, introduce yourself and start a conversation with any one of the guides, healers, doctors, coaches, and human beings authored in this book that resonated with you. Reach out, share your story, and connect. They want to know you and co-create with you.

While each of us has our own sacred space, we are intertwined and connected in a larger quantum field of energy, it is in that space where we can choose to support each other, and as I like to say, cheer each other on!

You may have tried many tools and approaches to help make shifts in your life, or achieve specific goals. You may have witnessed a friend or college achieve a goal you would like to achieve, but when you take the exact steps they did you don't achieve the same progress. Many get excited about starting a new practice or experience they believe will take them where they want to go, only to realize it's difficult to stay committed or the practice doesn't seem to work for you. Cheers to you for trying new things and never giving up. I love witnessing determination and perseverance.

I have an amazing life coach (*Wendi, thank you*), because in order to live my best most authentic life, improve myself, stay in alignment with my purpose and focused on where I want to grow, I need support. Partnering with a coach enhances my perspective and experiences, and for me turns up the volume on my inner voice and "aha" moments.

No one knows you like you do, and there is no doubt you are your own best healer, coach, guide, teammate. Close your eyes for a moment and tune into that knowing, the knowing that you have all you need already inside you. Feel your body breathe itself. Hear your heart beat. Embrace your uniqueness. Recall moments when you showed up for yourself. Smile and celebrate you.

"Rely on yourself, and be true to who you are. What's unique about you is what will take you far. Don't look to others to say you're okay. You know it – so believe it! – show your own self the way."

– Wayne Dyer

But here's the deal, to make impactful changes, the expertise of a guide, skilled coach, doctor, or topic expert can enable you to stay accountable, focused and supported knowing someone is in your corner cheering you on and challenging your limiting beliefs. They will help you rediscover and shine your light on the important thoughts, beliefs, values, purpose, strengths, and areas of weakness that are uniquely you.

When you partner with the right guide or coach, the one that knows you are the expert in your life and meets you where you are with deep curiosity and desire to co-create with you, you are more likely to follow your dreams, enhance what you want to focus on, adopt something new, travel, and explore new solutions, and shift away from limiting practices and into a sustainable life you love. The partnership can be magical and impactful changes happen. It's there you find the alignment of mind, body, and soul, and you can heal faster, and truly embody what lights you up.

I encourage you to explore and hire a coach or guide if you are feeling like something in your life is missing, you feel stuck, trapped in negative feelings, need a refresh, are looking for what your passion and purpose are, want to live your best life, sleep better, or increase energy. Find your guide, cheerleader, or expert who wants to team up with you. This book includes human beings who have journeyed through some of these experiences and are passionate about sharing and creatively engaging with others to help them embrace and shine their passion. Ultimately finding what uniquely works for them.

The time is now to come out from under what's been holding you back from taking the steps toward living the life you deserve. What would it feel like to have the support and guidance you want? What would life look like if you felt in charge of your life? What if you knew your purpose and had someone dedicated to helping you feel aligned to it?

I like to say practice makes better practice, but you have to start, and starting can feel scary, but starting with a guide or coach can feel exciting and hopeful. As a coach, I know one thing, when my clients are evolving and growing, so am I, and that's what lights me up!

I hope you enjoyed this book, and I hope it inspired to you try something new or maybe look at something in a new way. I would love to hear from you and get to know what you are up to, how you are evolving and where you could use guidance. Please find me at www.subtle-shifts.com and set up a time to connect.

As a first time author, if you enjoyed or gained anything from this book, I would love your feedback. Please consider leaving a review on Amazon. It supports all of the authors who bravely wrote their story for this book and helps create awareness so others can find the stories and tools too!

Lastly, please know, the love and light in me, sees and honors the love and light in you.

Shine bright,

Colleen

OVERFLOWING WITH GRATITUDE

"Being grateful is contagious! When someone says "thank you"
to you, you are happier and then you spread that happiness to
others, ultimately the happiness gets spread across the world.
It's like dropping a pebble in a pond.
The ripple from the dropped pebble affects the whole pond."

– Finn Avis

This is a piece of a speech our son shared with his school in fourth grade. His powerful words are part of my daily mantra as they remind me that even the smallest ounce of gratitude creates wide reaching impacts and raises the vibrations of kindness and acceptance.

So, imagine the gratitude for a group of amazing human beings that came together to share their inspiring stories and personal tools. Sacred Space authors, there aren't many words that can express my tremendous gratitude to each of you for taking this journey together. Because of each of you, we did it, we got vulnerable, we forged new connections, and we created a ripple that could not have been created without each of your individual contributions. Thank you for your bravery and sharing so generously. Thank you for being you.

Laura, I now know why you call your company Brave Healer Productions. Becoming an author, while at moments was hard and required bravery, indeed is a healing process. Thank you for creating the sacred space to bring this collective book to life, for helping me grow, practice being brave, and for holding my hand throughout this entire process. I was learning every step of the way, and your expertise allowed me to trust the process, and your guidance offered me the space to relax when things felt too big for me.

Alex, thank you for checking in on me every step of the way, it meant more than you will ever know, and your timing was always perfect.

Dino, your beautiful book cover creates a perfect first impression of our book. Thank you for taking the time to listen to my ideas and to translate them into something even better. I appreciate you, your professionalism and making our book shine inside and out.

To all our friends, family, colleagues, acquaintances and book launch team members who supported us during the writing, publishing, launching and promoting of this project, thank you so much for your support, love, words of encouragement, and purchases.

Readers, just like dessert I always save the best for last. You are the best, and this was all worth it because you showed up. Thank you! Thank you for exploring each chapter, being brave, curious, and willing to try new tools, craft them into your own approach and shining your light! Thank you for reading our stories with an open mind, compassionate heart, and kindness. Keep reaching for what is divinely yours, follow the fun and raise the collective vibration with your unique subtle shifts.

"I have come to realize this truth:
some of the greatest impacts we can make in our lives
start with subtle shifts.
Subtle shifts that taken one purposeful step at a time,
in the direction of honoring ourselves,
trusting our most inner wisdom,
reveal our most sacred spaces."

– Colleen Avis